PARACELSUS

PARACELSUS.

PARACELSUS

Monarch of Medicine

ANDREW SUSAC

Doubleday & Company, Inc.
Garden City, New York

*This one's for
Paul Susac,
one of my sons*

LIBRARY OF CONGRESS CATALOG CARD NUMBER 71–76552
COPYRIGHT © 1969 BY ANDREW SUSAC

CONTENTS

I

THEO, THE BOY

Throughout his life, a man cannot cast off that which he has received in his youth. My share was harshness, as against the subtle, prudish, superfine. Those who were brought up in soft clothes and by womenfolk have little in common with us who grew up among the pine trees.

PARACELSUS

1

I T WAS THE HOUR between daylight and dark, the magic hour of a spring evening, A.D. 1502. The sounds of the Swiss village of Einsiedeln had faded away. The moon, not quite full, hanging over the jagged Alps was spilling its light into the snow-covered valley—really spilling it. To the boy the light had weight, it pressed against the snow. He could *hear* it. It was a kind of game with Theo—he listened for the small sounds, a sleepy cricket maybe, or the wind-blown call of a crow. Only this night he heard a bigger sound from below, the faint clatter of hoofs, two horses drumming over Devil's Bridge and, suddenly louder, pounding round the bend beyond the clump of fir trees and then, each hoof distinct, struggling up the little hill and pulling up short—could it be?—at the hitching post just outside.

Theo was finishing his last chore before bed. He was listening, but his hands were filling the jars of his father's kit of *arcana*, secret medicines of brown powders and pink

salts and ivory grains. His father, Dr. Wilhelm von Hohenheim, stood in his long yellow smock at a table, his finger
on the huge page of a manuscript. His mother Elsa was
at the fireplace stirring some herb decoction whose "virtue"
Dr. Wilhelm would try on himself before he turned in.
Elsa had been skittish since moonrise, for she knew that
a "hunchbacked" moon invited bad spirits. As the horses
pulled up whinnying and neighing, she instinctively made
the sign of the cross.

Dr. Wilhelm looked up. Theo set down the jar he was
holding and ran to the middle of the three frame windows.
He looked hard into the half-light; then, just to make
sure, looked again.

"It's him, the baron!" he said excitedly. "It's Baron
Sigmund, Papa!"

The ladle in Elsa's hands dropped to the fireplace.

"It's all right, Elsa, I'll get it," said the doctor, and
went to the door. But before he could grasp the brass
knob, the door burst open and knocked him back against
the table. A squire-at-arms, sword drawn, had thrown the
door open and had stepped inside. Behind him, framed
in the doorway, was the baron. And in his arms, covered
with an embroidered silken quilt, was a girl, her long
yellow hair hanging to the floor. The baron had the look
of a wild man.

His lips were moving but no sound came. When the
words did come, all they said, over and over, was, "You
. . . you . . . you . . . !"

"She's dead then, little Greta?" asked Dr. Wilhelm.

"She's in the sleep of death," the squire said gruffly.
"Breath without life."

"Breath without life," repeated the baron, looking down
helplessly at the girl.

"Then she's alive!" said Dr. Wilhelm, springing into action. "Why in the name of heaven do you *stand* there?" Before the baron could react, the doctor, quickly but gently, took the limp body of the girl. And suddenly he was giving orders to everybody.

"Elsa, make ready the cot. Hot water, Theo, quickly. And snow, snow for the blade. And you," he said to the squire, a beefy fellow with shaggy black eyebrows, "push shut the door."

The squire, who was not very bright, looked at the doctor and blinked.

"Push shut the door," repeated the doctor, raising his voice a bit. He didn't speak loudly, the doctor; he didn't have to. When he meant business, there was something in his voice that brooked no nonsense. The squire pushed the door shut with his free hand; but he didn't put his sword back into its scabbard.

Sigmund von Beck, a wealthy and powerful man, could afford the best. So when his only child Greta, as she was helping her father into his hunting gear, accidentally pierced the calf of her leg with an arrow, Sigmund sent Karl, the squire, posthaste to the University of Basel. It was there that Professor Hermann Spiegel held forth on medicine. The professor had a reputation throughout Europe for brilliance—not, it is true, in the handling of wounds but in the handling of words.

He spoke wittily. He outclassified Aristotle, the ancient Greek whose word was law in science. And he could take either side, the pro or the con, of any point in medicine and carry the day. As for the unlearned barber-surgeons, he could level the most practiced with the arch of an eyebrow. Besides, didn't he have the biggest library in all of Germany? And he *was* head of the department. Flat-tered to be asked and anxious to do his friend Sigmund a good turn, Professor Spiegel buckled right down to work.

First he consulted his *Galen,* the authoritative text of the day. Galen, a Roman physician by then dead thirteen hundred years, prescribed a mixture of three dozen earths and herbs, including ground whale tooth, snake fat, and the feathers and excreta of a baby eagle; and all this the professor with his own hands molded into a doughy pad or poultice.

Next, he consulted the university astrologer for a look at the heavenly signs. The house of the zodiac which rules over the calves is Aquarius, the Water Bearer—a wet sign. This naturally called for a wet poultice. But as it turned out, the planet Mars was in Aquarius, and Mars is harmful in matters of healing; so treatment would have to wait until Mars moved out of Aquarius—three days.

And last, being a religious man, the professor had his assistant fetch from an apothecary a powder made from the shinbone of St. Chrysostom, on whose day Greta had hurt herself. And he sent this assistant, his most promising scholar, to administer the poultice, with the instructions that if Greta were of a "sanguine" temper, he might bleed her one- and one-half cups, neither more nor less. But under no circumstance was he to apply the poultice until Mars was safely out of Aquarius.

Within a week Greta's leg was red and swollen, the wound festering; there was a huge lump under the knee. Her face was flushed with fever, her eyes glazed. But the assistant, under strict orders from his master, had applied the poultice, bled the leg one- and one-half cups, taken a dozen gold ducats for his pains, and had returned to Basel. Baron Sigmund had no choice—he was obliged to call in the local doctor—what was his name?—"von" Hohenheim.

So now, in Dr. Wilhelm's house, the baron was not disposed to like doctors, any doctor, and particularly this commoner who pretended to nobility by prefixing his name with a "von."

Elsa, who was a nurse's assistant when Dr. Wilhelm met her, had placed a cot against the wall and stood ready with a flat wooden bowl. Theo stood by with scissors and a razor-sharp knife, whose hooked point was chilled in snow. Dr. Wilhelm laid Greta on the cot, exposed the wounded calf and with the scissors cut away the bandages. It was an ugly gash—especially the top half where a mound of pus was showing through the skin. Dr. Wilhelm's practiced fingers took up the knife. But instead of proceeding, he turned to the baron.

"The sword," he said, pointing at the squire with the knife, "must wait outside."

The baron glared at Dr. Wilhelm who, on one knee beside the cot, simply waited for Karl to leave.

"Karl!" The squire presented his sword. "Outside," said the baron. Again Karl seemed not to understand, so the baron said it again, this time savagely: *"Outside!"* Karl vanished.

"You took away the poultice," he said accusingly.

Dr. Wilhelm, who was about to make a retort, caught himself. He had no authority to remove the baron from the room, but he was not required to bicker. Besides, it was contrary to the doctors' oath.

Wilhelm and Elsa, doctor and nurse, swung into action. Elsa slipped the wooden bowl under the calf and then, using her thumbs, gently pulled the skin taut over the mound of pus. Immediately the knife was there, the doctor drawing the hooked point between: pus burst through and trickled down the calf into the bowl. And Greta's lips moved; she uttered her first sound in four days. She groaned.

At a bound the baron leaped forward and knocked the knife from Dr. Wilhelm's hands. It clattered to the floor. The two men rose, squared off like mortal enemies. "Doctors!" said the baron with a sneer. "If the girl lives, it's your miraculous powers. If she dies, it is the will of God!"

"Von Beck," said Dr. Wilhelm in a voice Theo had never heard. "You will sit across the room, on the window seat, or you will remove your person from my house."

The baron was stunned. Never before from a commoner, as he secretly regarded Dr. Wilhelm (even though Wilhelm's father—but not his mother—was of noble birth), had he heard such authority. He picked up the knife which he had knocked from the doctor's hand; then, changing his mind, he dropped it at the doctor's feet. But shrugging his shoulders, he moved over to the windows.

Elsa by now had cleaned the wound with vinegar and warm water. She removed the bowl, which was full of soiled bandages and waste fluids, and applied fresh bandages. Gently she straightened out the leg, wet the girl's parched lips with ice water and pulled the cover up to Greta's neck. Then the doctor moved in. He thumbed open an eyelid and put his ear to the girl's chest. Satisfied, he stood over her for a minute, watching her breath flow in and out, in and out. "Good," he whispered to Elsa. "The breath comes easier. She has a chance."

There was nothing to do now but wait. The doctor went over to the fireplace and ladled out a sample of the herb broth. Elsa sat at the head of the cot, humming a hymn to the Virgin Mother and, from time to time, putting to

Greta's brow a folded cloth soaked in snow. Two or three times, when the girl's head tossed, Elsa lifted it and spooned some apple brandy into Greta's mouth—with no effect. Baron Sigmund, his hands clasped behind him, stood like a statue, unmoving, and stared morosely out the window. After a while, Elsa stopped humming the hymn. The only sounds were the crazy whine of the wind down the chimney, and the boots of the squire pounding the planks of the porch.

Minutes grew and died. An hour passed.

"I'm hungry!" A tiny voice had come out of the air.

The baron seemed to fly across the room; he was kneeling at the side of the cot.

"Who are these people, Father?" demanded the girl, her wide eyes, a bit sunken, peering around. "Where are we? I'm hungry!"

Sigmund let out a roar of laughter, but a tear had already rolled into his blond beard. "Did you hear that? My Greta is hungry! Karl!" Before he had finished calling, Karl was inside.

Against Dr. Wilhelm's protests, the baron lifted the girl, blanket and all, and set her with great care in the squire's arms. "The girl is hungry, Karl, you hear it? Hungry!"

Suddenly he realized that his actions in the doctor's house had been less than noble. He looked over at Wilhelm who, seated on a stool at the fireside, was pouring himself a tankard of the broth. But Theo, standing nearby, was handier. The baron held toward the boy a small leather pouch, jingling it and saying, "For your father, boy." Theo, his eyes glaring, backed away. "My hand in friendship then," said the baron, extending his arm. In response, without out for a minute taking his eyes from the baron's, Theo put his hands behind his back.

Sigmund was vastly amused. "This one," he said, bellowing with laughter, "if this one doesn't die young, he'll die a hero." And he tossed the pouch of coins across the room to Dr. Wilhelm's feet.

"When am I going to eat?" Greta commanded. She was already almost her old self.

"Soon, Flower, soon," said the baron, laughing again. "Karl," he said, taking the girl, "you ride ahead. Tell the kitchen that Sigmund's daughter hungers—a whole lamb, freshly barbecued." Before Karl could turn to go out, the money pouch fell at his feet. The baron turned to see Theo's father holding up a single gold coin. "This much I earned, Your Lordship. The rest belongs to God."

"Von Hohenheim, I salute you," said the baron, subtly emphasizing the "von," his voice respectful for the first time that evening. "First thing tomorrow I'll offer it at High Mass."

"Better still, Sigmund," said Wilhelm accepting the compliment, "scatter the coins among the serfs outside your gates."

But the baron, whose treatment of his serfs was a scandal even among the noblemen, soured at the suggestion. "You mind your potions, Dr. Hohenheim," he said now, forgetting the "von." "Leave politics to me." With Greta in his arms, he wheeled and walked out, leaving the door open behind him. Theo closed it.

For the first time since Theo heard the hoofs, his father was grinning. "You are certainly right to scorn a doctor's life, my boy. One minute a charlatan, the next a god. And then, a charlatan again." He was stirring the tankard to avoid a mouthful of dregs at the bottom.

"Never, Father," said Theo passionately. "Never will I be a doctor!"

"Never, Theo?" said his father, suddenly serious again. "If you mean 'never,' you best not hate it. Hatred and love—they're magic—for we become the things we hate, my boy." He tossed off the bitter drink and shuddered. "As we become the things we love."

He was smiling.

2

A T THE BREAK of the next day Theo was already
mounted on a brown-and-white spotted pony—waiting in the morning mist for Dr. Wilhelm.

It was the day of Saturn and, ever since the weather
broke, it had been Theo's job Saturdays to load the kit
across the brown mare and to assist his father on his daily
rounds. Today they would go directly to the von Beck
castle, which was some five miles outside Einsiedeln, and
look in on a half-dozen other patients on the way back.
Only, on this particular morning Theo sensed something
was amiss.

For one thing, there was the hushed talk between Dr.
Wilhelm and Elsa. His parents were suddenly quiet when
he came within earshot. And for another, there was a busy
feeling in the air, despite the early hour—unseen carpenters
were pounding down below, and woodcutters were at work
everywhere around him, the sounds of their hacking echo-
ing from several sides. Wilhelm, wearing the traditional

doctor's garb—gray cloak with the collar of flat brown fur—
came out the door and down the flight of wooden stairs.
He turned and spoke to Elsa who appeared at the doorway.
Now Theo could make out their words.

"Such nonsense, Wilhelm."

"The boy can stay."

"Ach!" said Elsa, wiping the palms of her hands on the
long white apron. "And ruin his day?"

Wilhelm relented. "In any case we will be back in time.
Midafternoon at the latest."

"So then, you Hohenheim boys," said Elsa, "be off with
you." It always gave her a surge of joy to see "her boys,"
as she called Wilhelm and Theo, ride off together.

Decided now, Wilhelm mounted, reined his mare about,
and clucked her down the steep incline. Theo on his pony
waved to his mother and followed. He had managed some
thirty yards when he heard, "Theo?" It was his mother's
voice. Trying to bring his pony about, Theo called out.

"What is it, Mama?"

Elsa paused. "Nothing, Theo, it's nothing," she said, and
after another pause, called out, "There's cheesecake when
you're back."

Theo succeeded in bringing his pony round. He started
to give her a happy wave at the news, but by the time he
looked, the door was closed. She was gone.

More pounding echoed up from the village green and he
thought, "A platform, that's it. They're building a platform." But why? "A festival!" he murmured with a rush of
joy, but immediately shook his head. "Shrove Tuesday is
over."

"What's happening today, Papa?" he said aloud. But
Wilhelm had ridden out of range of answering. In any
case, Theo was about to discover for himself. The mist was

fast dissolving. He saw woodcutters with bundles of wood on their backs, converging on the green; and there in the center of the green was the platform—a platform of three levels built around a stake. Riding alongside his father now, he stole a glance: Wilhelm was riding stiffly, as though smoldering inside, looking neither to the left nor to the right. And suddenly it all fit into place—the hushed talk, the cutting and the pounding, his mother's odd good-by. At sundown that night, there was going to be a burning.

"But, Papa, *who?*" said Theo. Wilhelm and Elsa made it a rule to keep such news from the boy.

"Maria Reppeler."

"Crazy Mary!" thought Theo, and the picture of her came into his head—the sharp chin, the wart on the left cheekbone, the weird glint in her close-set eyes. Ever since her son died a half-dozen years back while fighting the Turks, Crazy Mary had lived alone in a decrepit house outside the village. She had a walnut tree which grew next to the fence, so that some of the nuts often fell in the road. When the children of the village filched these walnuts, she chased them away with a stick and with many a curse. Last year the burgomeister's twin girls had picked a bonnetful each, while Crazy Mary, in a rapture of profanity, cursed them through the slats of the fence. The next morning, as the whole village knew, the girls broke out with pox. In two weeks one of the girls was dead and the other, although she later recovered, was scarred for life.

"How can they tell *for sure* if she's bewitched?" Theo asked.

"How can they tell for sure *they're* not bewitched, these fathers who will burn her?" answered Wilhelm heatedly. Theo had read his mind. "Ideas are like air—some pure,

some pestilential," Wilhelm continued. He seemed to be
trying to figure it out for himself. "Some pestilences, like
this"—he waved his hand back toward the green—"this
thing tonight, work through the minds. Whole villages, you
see, my boy? An entire people in one swoop! An epidemic
of the mind," he said in a kind of muted agony. "The
mind! And who can heal the mind?"

"Who can heal the mind?" The words filled Theo's head.
But before he could respond, Wilhelm brought his heels
smartly into the sides of the mare, and she broke into an
easy gallop. Theo was again obliged to keep up. Past the
houses they rode, where here and there a six-inch layer of
snow was still clinging to the roofs. They crossed over
Devil's Bridge that spanned the rapids of the Siehl River,
went past two fenced-in pastures, made a quick right turn
past Crazy Mary's house; then abruptly Wilhelm reined
his mare to a halt.

"No use to run," he said. "The girl is all right." He
pointed to the sky. "The baron is out hunting this morning." Overhead was one of Sigmund's falcons gliding in a
wide circle, lazily, flicking a wing here and there to ride
gusts of the wind. Suddenly the circle closed; the bird
pulled in its wings and like an unlit meteor plummeted to
earth. It disappeared to the left of them behind a huge
rock. There was a quick shriek, the last cry of a hare.

They rode on at an easy trot, and Theo said, "What if
the girl had died? What could the baron do?"

Wilhelm shrugged his shoulders. His mouth grew hard.
After a bit he said, "Barons are men, Theo. Part animal,
part angel."

"He said you took a 'poultice' from her," said the boy.

"That is a medical term, a word for doctors. And you
don't want to be a doctor."

"What is a poultice?" Seeing the wry grin on his father's face, Theo was a bit sullen now. He didn't like to be teased, even gently.

"A poultice is a pancake, boy. Only not so tasty." They were jogging along, riding into the sun with a fresh wind in their faces. "A poultice," he said, turning the word over in his mind. "It's like this, Theo. When doctors are sure of the disorder and the treatment, we use one thing. One particular dose in one particular way. One medicine for one disorder. When we're *not* sure, why then, we use a poultice. When we don't know enough medicine, we resort to the law of averages, and a poultice represents our law of averages. A poultice, you see, is three dozen treatments in one. A spoonful of mold from bones, a handful of pigeon dung, a pinch of mummy powder, some feathers and furs and skins, and there you are! All this we gather when the moon is right, we knead into a paste or maybe a mud cake, and—when the moon is right again—we spread it on the patient where it hurts!"

Theo, laughing, said, "Why didn't the baron have a surgeon sew it up and be done with it? Wasn't it that simple?"

"Yes and no, Theo," said Wilhelm, "depending on the surgeon. Here's where we are, in this world of healing. On the one hand we have doctors of medicine. Witty fellows. Splendidly arrayed—long red capes and furs and rings. Armed with the complete education, six to eight years of disquisitions and disputations and dissertations. Yet the sight of a carbuncle on their own necks makes them retch." Theo laughed aloud. He loved this vein. "All right, boy, laugh. But remember," Wilhelm said, "you're laughing at your father." And Theo laughed all the more. "And do these hypercultured peacocks know their business? Well, how can they? Do they deliver babies? They do not. Do they set broken bones—or close a wound? Beneath their stations. Why, I myself know a dozen doctors so exalted, they haven't so much as met a patient face to face! You scowl, my son, but it's quite true. It's their assistants who do the actual treatments. A perfect system, don't you see? Patient recovers, it's the doctor's knowledge; patient dies, it's the assistant's bungling." By now Theo was howling with delight.

"Then on the other hand, we have our barber-surgeons. These are a caution too, in their own right. *Barber*-surgeons, boy. You think about it. Doesn't it sound strange? The main job of the man who bleeds our veins, pulls our teeth, mends our flesh—and for that matter hacks an occasional bone—is to trim our beards! But why? Why are these vital duties left to barbers? Simply because they happen to have the tools. And what about this bloody-winged crow? Is he good at his craft? Well, for the first few cases, maybe the first few dozens, certainly not; he's learning. The human body is full of little surprises. But later on, after a dozen fractures, a dozen amputations, he catches on. Chances are good he'll find the vein, the joint, he'll sew the proper parts the first time round."

Theo was laughing so hard he slumped forward to the pony's mane.

"So there you are, my boy. The doctor who cannot stand the sight of blood and the barber-surgeon who loves no other sight so much." Then, unexpectedly, Wilhelm's voice grew serious, almost reverent. "You choose your own way, Theo, but let me say—of all the pursuits of man, I know of none more noble than my own."

They had been making their way up a mountain path, past three ground swells filled with sharpened pikes. They were approaching a moat at the castle door which was hidden behind a huge, seamless iron plate—the drawbridge. They hadn't properly stopped when a head poked through a slit above this plate.

"What is your business, strangers?" the man called down.

"Physician to the little baroness. Wilhelm von Hohenheim . . ." Wilhelm nudged the boy.

"And Theophrastus," the boy blurted. He was a bit rattled.

"Son and assistant," added Wilhelm.

The head disappeared. The man's voice rang out, "Wilhelm von Hohenheim and son, physicians!" and three other voices, each more distant than the one before, repeated the words. They waited for the command to pass them, but nothing came. A quarter hour, then a half went by. The horses, restless, stamped and wheezed. Father and son, standing there, had become chilled to the bone when, with the clanking of chains, the drawbridge squeaked down across the narrow but very deep moat. They prepared to enter.

But two squires on brightly caparisoned mounts blocked their way. Between the squires, afoot, was the glittering figure of a courtier. Dressed in tights, a flaring doublet and a cape, he reflected all the colors of the rainbow. He removed his headpiece, a flat, square beret with a foot-long purple plume, and made a profound bow.

"There is some mistake, my worthies," he said, rising. His speech was so elegant, it was offensive.

"There is no mistake, sir," said Wilhelm. "Only last night . . ."

"But I assure you, my good Dr. Hohenheim, there is. The baroness has a physician."

"Professor Hermann Spiegel?"

"The same. Thanks to the great professor, the baroness is still alive today.

Wilhelm waited a bit and said, "This from Baron Sigmund?"

Already the chains were clanking to raise the drawbridge. "Sigmund von Beck has spoken," announced the courtier, again in his profound bow. The four serfs leaning into the handles of a huge spoked wheel took in the chain. They disappeared from view, squires, courtier and all, and Wilhelm and the boy were left staring again at the blank iron plate.

They rode in silence to the other patients on the doctor's rounds. All of them were Sigmund's serfs who lived in cottages nearby; and all were recovering smoothly. Five of the six, as "the good doctor" left, thrust a little something into Theo's hands by way of a fee. Serfs, especially Sigmund's, had no silver or gold, so they were obliged to pay in produce. By the time they left the last of the patients, Theo had collected a plucked rooster, three small cheeses, and eight or nine eggs wadded with straw in a net of homespun.

The sun was scarcely a full degree past meridian when the doctor said, "Home, Theo, and in good time." Then, noticing the "gifts," he said. "You thanked them graciously?" Theo adjusted the eggs, which he had hung from the pommel of his saddle, and nodded.

Wilhelm set the mare to a steady pace. He was thinking of the eggs. And Theo, his eyes on the assortment of food which he carried, couldn't quite catch up; he was obliged to dodge the specks of mud flung up by the mare's rear hoofs. The first chance he got, when the road widened a bit, he spurred the pony gently and pulled alongside.

"Bar-rooom!" From the thatched cottage ahead, the last

before Crazy Mary's, came the blast of gunpowder. A puff of blue smoke squirted out the rear window. The door nearest the road burst open and out rushed an old crone carrying a smoking blunderbuss. At her heels was Adolf Schwartzkopf, the cantankerous, choleric peasant who owned the house. Almost everybody avoided Adolf; he was convinced that water on the body before the spring equinox brought on plague.

"Save me, Doctor, for the love of God," said the old woman. In spite of the fact that she was toothless, she made her words perfectly clear.

"Stonehead! Sorceress! Sow! It's *I* will save you," said Adolf, who had picked up a piece of kindling wood. "For the devil I'll save you!"

"Calm, Adolf, calm," said Wilhelm, dismounting and coming between them. "Now then, Anya," he said to the crone, "suppose you tell me first."

Adolf's wife, Frieda, was about to give birth to their first child. Anya, a midwife, had been called in to attend the birth. After ten hours, the old woman explained, she had become concerned. Things were going entirely too slowly to suit her, especially considering the fact that, as everybody knew, Adolf was a confirmed tightwad. Besides, she had another delivery on the other side of Einsiedeln to attend. So she decided to use a wonderful new technique, just developed at the university, for hurrying things along: as Frieda was slipping off into a short but much-needed nap, Anya whipped the blunderbuss from under her apron, set the cone-shaped muzzle at the expectant mother's left ear, and pulled the trigger. But instead of delivering the babe, the charge set Frieda wild. The last either of them saw of her, she was trying to pull herself high enough to climb out of the bedroom window.

Wilhelm promptly lifted the blunderbuss out of the old girl's hands. "You may pick it up from the burgomeister's in the morning," he said, and hurried into the house.

"Quack!" screamed Anya, and spit at him. Adolf had followed Wilhelm in to calm Frieda, so there was nobody to hate but Theo; and for a minute or two she stood there looking at the boy with burning eyes. "His sssson!" she said, hissing like an enraged goose, saying the words as though with them she had cursed the world; then she waddled down the road toward Einsiedeln.

Theo was used to long waits, but this was the longest he could remember. Hours went by, he was sure. Clouds gathered overhead to the west. Hesperus, the evening star, came out, although the sun still burned through a cloud. From time to time Adolf bustled out, talking to himself or cursing between his teeth; he picked up some kindling or fetched another pail of water and, still jabbering, rushed back inside. But he said nothing to the boy.

Orange streamers of sunlight filtered through the western clouds.

"Waa-ah!" A new sound came from the house. "At last!" thought Theo. Wilhelm appeared at the doorway, rolling down his sleeves, and behind him, Adolf, who rushed forward, grabbed the doctor's hand and pumped it. Overjoyed, Adolf rushed back inside, reappeared with four medium-sized onions and put them into Theo's hands. Then, reconsidering, he took back one.

Wilhelm was already mounted and had turned the mare toward home. He was worried. "Ride fast, boy. Save what you can."

"Papa, the eggs . . ." Theo began, but Wilhelm cut him off.

"Shhh!" he said. "Did you hear that?" And as he spoke

Theo heard a woman's voice, high and shrill, coming from the village. "Crazy Mary, Papa?"

"It's early, Theo, early." Then Wilhelm startled his son. He took the boy by the shoulders, digging his fingers into them so that they hurt, and said:

"You make it home alone, boy, hear me? Stop nowhere." He strapped the mare who bolted into a gallop, and shouted it again over his shoulder. "Stop nowhere!"

Theo was dumbfounded. He watched the figure of his father dwindle into the distance. Then he reached down and gave his pony a pat on the side of his neck, and with a "tchik-tchik" turned him toward home. Maybe it was the wide, wide sky above him, resplendent now with color, or maybe the high reach of the mountain peaks or the brisk wind, but something made him shudder; a wave of electricity trickled up his spine. He had never been so happy.

For the first time in his life Theo was on his own.

3

NOT ONLY WAS the boy happy, he *knew* he was happy. And knowing it made a difference. Everything around him seemed to be perfect, seemed somehow to be more alive. Off to his left, in a pasture, a rounded white mass of limestone, pink now in the sunset, appeared to glow from an inside light. A clump of bluebells at the edge of the road seemed almost to speak.

Something in him yearned upward, he wanted to give himself to the sky; and looking up he saw a lone stork flying straight toward him. Its wings pumped the air so effortlessly, he was sure that it had been flying so since the beginning of time.

"Whoa, Pico," he said. When the bird was directly overhead, something—maybe the stiff feet or the ungainly beak, maybe the graceful struggle of the wings—made him laugh aloud. The laugh startled Pico; he darted forward and almost set Theo tumbling into the mud. And Theo, now that he had a reason, really set to laughing. He felt the sound of his laughter filling the countryside, as Pico whinnied in response.

But as suddenly as this happiness had come, it disappeared.

Just ahead was the roadside shrine, Our Black Lady of Einsiedeln. Theo never had been able to look "Our Lady" straight in the eye. The nameless craftsman who had carved Virgin and Child out of a huge crystal of black quartz had put something or left something dreadful in the face. And now, in order to trot by, he touched a heel to the pony's ribs.

But scarcely was he alongside when a fearsome feeling enveloped him and, kicking the pony's flanks sharply, he bounded down the road. Away he went, and away, galloping full tilt, trying to outdistance Our Black Lady, trying to shake the horror. Just ahead loomed Crazy Mary's house—it would be a refuge; but as he came by he remembered that his mother Elsa had been her playmate years ago, had played no doubt on the very spot he rode, and the thought served to deepen the horror. The reins fell from his fingers. He dug his fingers into the pony's mane and held on. He pushed inward with his knees and crushed several of the eggs, so that Pico's flank and his own foot trailed a string of slime. Onward they raced, the pony and the boy, until Pico's hoofs clattered onto Devil's Bridge. There, without prompting from Theo, the pony pulled up short.

Pico, frothing, pawed the air with his front hoofs. He whinnied and tossed his head to the left, down river.

Somebody three cascades below on the Siehl River was lighting a fire or a torch. Theo could make out the forms of four men in shallow water, and on shore, a fifth whom he knew—knew but could not place. Just now he was too

excited and exhausted to think. What were they doing
down there? And who was the fifth, familiar man? The
feeling of horror was gone now, though a deep uneasiness
remained. Thankfully, he clucked Pico into a trot and,
reins again in hand, moved on.

He made the bend in the road below which would be the
village green. And there a new sound, separating itself
from the Siehl cascades, came up to him. Again he was
shocked. Wasn't Crazy Mary to be burned alive within the
hour? But the sounds which came up to him were sounds
of festival, of fun!

The sight was unforgettable. At the far end of the green,
the three levels of platform had been neatly overlaid with
faggots. All of them pointed to the stake. And hordes of
people, far more than he had ever seen in the Einsiedeln
green, were jostling their way to and from the half-dozen
stands thrown up for the occasion.

On a stump in the farthest corner stood a figure in a
long brown habit with hood—Brother Ignatius, the friar
out of Zurich who, Theo knew, was peddling indulgences
and relics. Ignatius had a wide variety of teeth and bones
and clothes for any saint's day. He had a dozen splinters
from the pastor's crook of St. Peter, blessed by Pope Alex-
ander IV himself; he had a jagged patch from St. Veronica's
veil, with not only the blood and sweat of Jesus (the smell
of sweat, miraculously, was still very strong), but with the
outline of the right nostril showing; and enclosed in a
glass bubble, he had a bit of the dung from the horse
which had thrown St. Paul on his way to Damascus. Just
the touch of this bubble, said Ignatius, had worked many a
miracle of healing.

From an oxcart directly below the boy, Tomaso the
Tuscan was selling bad wine, the awful stuff which every

spring for five years he had tried, unsuccessfully, to pawn off on the villagers. Tomaso's wine was a local joke. He had used green wood in the making of his casks, and the grape juice, fermenting, had "drawn out the wormwood." It was bitter as alkali. Yet there the vintner was, unloading mugs and jugs of the stuff without so much as turning off the wooden spigot between customers.

Across the way, a troupe of *commedia dell' arte* players, en route from Naples to Vienna, had stopped over an extra night to catch the crowd. They had chained their bear to the eye ring in the center of a festooned platform on wheels, their portable stage; and as one of the troupe baited the bear with a pointed staff, two or three acrobats, one of them, a girl, would tumble or cartwheel or handspring onto the stage and then out of danger. Three girls of ten or so circulated among the crowd, collecting coppers and silvers in their outstretched skirts.

The most commanding of the stands was the food concession. Old Man Schwartzert—Old Stickfingers, as the villagers secretly called him—the wily merchant who was head of the powerful merchant's guild, had his two black stallions pull a wagon flat right up to the platform itself. The wheels brushed the bottom row of faggots. And here Old Stickfingers offered a treat for every taste. On the flat were barrels of fish, pickled and smoked, and of pork cracklings; hanging from racks were strings of jerky, beef and pork and goat—smoked, peppered, and spiced, as well as bundles of onion and garlic and leek; and there was row after row of small fruit and meat and cottage cheese pies. His drawing card was the goatskin pouch full of an Oriental herb which, when stuffed into a tube and lit and drawn into the breath, not only healed all diseases of the lungs but induced a lasting state of happiness in one and all. In those who were truly in a state of grace, the fumes induced a vision of St. Michael the Archangel.

But what delighted and bewildered Theo most of all was the very middle of the green: there, to the gay sounds of lutes and flutes and horns, a dozen villagers—woodcutters mostly, with the uninhibited ladies of the Boars Tail Inn—were pumping their knees and swishing their skirts in a wild dance!

As he rode Pico down the steep incline onto the green, Theo could not take his eyes off the scene. It was unreal. Although the sun had set and only the last red splendor of its rays shone, the moon, perfectly full tonight, completely lit up the countryside. The torches which darted here and there in the crowd were not really necessary. *Could this,* thought the boy, *could this be a burning?*

And then he knew. He and Wilhelm had been mistaken. He was sure of it now. Yes, he could be happy again! A festival, this was a spring festival! Something unexpected and wonderful had happened. A new saint had been canonized. The emperor had declared an amnesty on all political prisoners. Isolde Wozzek, the rich spinster who had monopolized the cheese trade in the whole of Schwyz canton, had landed a man at last. Something had happened and he could enjoy the whole scene, the dancing, the tumbling, the food, the . . . What about the faggots, the three rises of platform? What about the stake with the three iron clamps? The lost feeling returned. Somewhere deep inside, deeper than his body, he was going to be sick.

Theo now had made his way directly to the stone building which served as the village prison. Unconsciously, as he puzzled over the sights before him, he had reined Pico; and at this moment the prison door opened. A wave of excited whispering, and then of silence, spread through the crowd. Four constables with Crazy Mary chained among them stepped onto the cobblestones. Crazy Mary, who had evidently refused to wear the customary black, wore a long robe of orange; and the constables, dressed in the uniform of the Pope's guard, carried a halberd in one hand, and in the other held one end of a chain which was welded to the iron belt about the witch's waist. The crowd gave way instinctively, so that Theo, atop Pico, stood in the way. It did not occur to the boy to move.

"Giddap," said one of the two front constables to Pico. But Pico obeyed only the voice of his master, and the boy was looking down as though from another world.

"Move the colt, boy," said another constable. Theo, still dazed, made no answer.

The two constables lowered their halberds to the boy's chest. They were about to give him another warning when Crazy Mary spoke.

"*Liebchen!*" she said, opening her arms up as if to an old friend. "You," she said, peering up into Theo's face, "are you Elsa's boy?"

"Wilhelm and Elsa, *ja*." Theo had found his voice.

"So strong," said Mary admiringly, to the constable at her right. "Such shoulders!" The constable gave no response, so she elbowed him savagely in the ribs.

"Strong, strong," grunted the constable.

"And pretty like a picture!" she said. Out of her toothless mouth erupted a wild, high cackle which stopped as suddenly as it had started. She was all business now; her brow knit and, leaning onto Pico's flank, she hissed up at the boy. "Wilhelm will help poor Mary." She looked around wildly. "Where is Herr Doctor Wilhelm?"

Unaccountably, the boy's mind flashed back to the

bridge, to the long coat of the fifth man. . . . But Mary was hissing up at him again.

"Please give Wilhelm thanks from the witch."

"I'll give it, Mary," the boy said.

"And Elsa, my darling Elsa," she said, again peering around. "Why didn't she come?"

But before the boy could answer, one constable touched the point of his halberd to Pico's belly and the colt bolted out of the way, scattering the crowd.

"A kiss, a kiss for Elsa, boy," screamed the old woman as the constables pulled her on her way.

Although the crowd obligingly kept clear the way to the stake, it immediately closed behind Mary and her guards. Scarcely had she been turned away from Theo when a *commedia* tumbler, somersaulting out of the crowd, landed in her path. He mimicked her walk perfectly for a dozen steps and then, wheeling, he stiffened into a human log and fell "dead." The crowd, including Mary, was delighted. A rain of coppers fell onto the green. With a burst of energy Mary picked up four of them before her guards could restrain her.

"What do you want with coppers, you old crone?" came a voice from the crowd. It was Heinrich, the village wag. One of the constables tried to wrest them from her hand, but he found Mary more than a match for him.

"Ach," said Heinrich, "let the old witch have them. She's got to give the devil his due!"

The crowd laughed nervously. Heinrich was always good for a cheap laugh, and any laughter encouraged him. So now he moved alongside her, as if for a chat.

"You chilly, Mary?" he said, speaking less to her than to his audience. There was a ripple of laughter. At his words Crazy Mary seemed to notice the cold; she clutched her arms and drew them into her body. "Don't worry, Crazy One," said Heinrich. "It's a hot night in hell!" At this the crowd laughed hugely.

Mary stiffened visibly and looked up.

"She's looking to the moon for help," Heinrich announced with a roar. Heinrich was having a field day.

"She's looking for demons," shouted a woman holding a little girl.

"No good," said Heinrich quickly. "No good, your demons now. Better a chisel for those chains. Better a little rain."

As the crowd roared its appreciation, Mary spoke directly to Heinrich in a normal tone. "Heinrich," she said, "you were always a fool."

"*Ja*, Mary, sure," said Heinrich, "but not so foolish that I'm going to burn."

"You'll burn, you'll roast in hell. Not Mary—you," she said. Suddenly she was shouting at the top of her lungs, addressing the whole crowd: "Not Crazy Mary burns in hell, but you! All of you! You'll turn upon a spit, you'll roast!" And again the high, strangely gay cackle seemed to fill the air.

This defiance was more to the crowd's liking. Now they could burn her in good conscience. Dozens of them, especially those along the path to the stake, surged in upon her with fists and sticks and staves. They moved with such force that the constables were obliged to fend not only for Mary, to save her for the burning, but for themselves. Hadn't she already killed one of the burgomeister's twins, and God knows how many more? And now, what gall—to threaten them openly, right then and there! She deserved whatever she got, and more! So violent was the crowd that when Mary reached the platform, the air seemed to be full of flying objects—fruit, relics, fish and pies.

But as Mary stepped onto the first level, Theo saw a strange thing happen. The old woman turned abruptly, she faced the crowd, standing utterly motionless as object after object pelted her. At last something soggy, the filling of a fruit pie perhaps, struck her forehead and slid slowly down her face. The crowd cheered; but when she disdained even to recognize it, the cheer died. Even Theo, whose sympathy was all with the old crone, could feel her scorn. And when the quiet came, she looked deliberately to the left and the right and then, lifting her hand, threw back the four coppers. No one picked them up; no one dared. Then, with no prodding from her captors, she mounted to the topmost level and set her spine against the stake.

In a moment the constables had removed their chains, each his own, and had clamped the old woman's body in three places—at the ankles, the waist and the throat. No time was lost. No sooner did the last lock click in the silence than torches from four directions were touched to the bottom row of faggots. At the sight of the flames, the general murmur began again. As the flames rose, so rose the noise of the crowd.

Higher and higher leaped the flames, a hungry circle of crimson, flickering into the sky until, to the dancing of the flames, the crowd, no longer a thousand different people, but one, enjoying and enduring a single passion, reached a pitch of horrible ecstasy. But Crazy Mary, whether from a new reach of self-control or mesmerized by the sights and sounds, moved not so much as a finger. Only her head fell back, as though to bask her face in the moon.

Tiny tongues of flame now touched the hem of her orange robe; quickly they ate their way upward, and the screams of the crowd once again echoed into nothing. They wanted and dreaded to hear the screams of torment as the witch died.

But no scream came. No sound from Mary came at all. Somebody in the garret window of a house beyond the stake was trying to quiet the wail of a baby. The only other sound was the crackle and the mounting roar of the flames. The figure behind the wall of red remained stock-still—so still in fact that, perhaps because the orange of her dress blended so well with the flames, it seemed for an instant that no one was there at all.

Then at last, after what seemed to Theo an entire age, a single, long, piercing shriek filled the whole Alpine valley. It seared itself forever on his brain. The strength drained out of him. He slumped forward in his saddle.

Feeling the reins free, Pico moved on, picking his way through the throng. With all his might, even as he hung there, Theo fought off this strangeness. He had something to do, something to remember. . . . Meantime, he was vaguely aware of feet moving confusedly, at cross purposes, the feet of women, the feet of men. He was aware too of a hand lifting one of his cheeses and, a scant minute later, of a knife a handbreadth under his eyes cutting loose the rooster which—strangely, he thought—did not reach the ground. *Robbery,* he thought, *I am being robbed.* But he didn't care. He was remembering the bridge, the fifth man. He had pieced it together at last. The fifth man in the long black coat with the fur collar, in the doctor's coat, was Wilhelm. Someone in the river had drowned. He had gone there on a call.

A new odor, the smell of burnt flesh, reached him from the village green. He retched.

When he came round, he found himself at the gate of

his own house. Pico, good pony, had found his own way. Wilhelm stood in the doorway.

"Theo," came his father's voice. It sounded hollow, tired.

"Yes, Papa, I'm here. The crowd . . . so many . . . stopped me." *The wind is picking up,* thought the boy. *Why doesn't he close the door behind him?*

"Theo," Wilhelm said again. He was working his mouth as if it were too dry to talk. The boy, who had never seen his father in such a state, started to laugh.

"I'm all right, Papa. . . ." Theo saw that it was something else. With all its force, the feeling of horror which had seized him at the shrine of Our Black Lady overwhelmed him again. His father had come down and ever so gently put his hands on the boy's shoulders.

"Theo . . . Theo . . ."

"Elsa is dead." He had never called his mother by her given name before.

"She's dead. Mama is dead," said Wilhelm softly, finally.

Inside, on the cot where Greta lay only the night before, lay the body of Elsa, wife of Wilhelm and mother of Theophrastus. Wilhelm had dressed the body in Elsa's long, yellow "sunshine" dress with the careful lacework. He had dried and combed her hair, trying to think how his wife would want her body to be seen for the last time by her son. To keep the blue eyes closed, he had put a small gold coin on each of the lids. And at the head on a stool flickered a lone candle. Theo saw what his father had done so tenderly, and yet the thought didn't move him at all. He felt nothing. His thoughts moved sluggishly, between long blanks. There was this strange, high ringing in his ears.

"Too late," he heard Wilhelm saying. "I reached the bridge too late. She waited there. Maria, burning, don't you

see? Too much. And so, she fell. . . . She jumped. . . ."
He shrugged his shoulders. But he could see the boy wasn't
listening. As the boy stood at the foot of the cot, his mind
was fixed on a thought of his own.

"Mama's become a thing," he said.

Too much for the boy, and all, all in one day, thought
Wilhelm. He feared for the worst. He watched Theo move
woodenly over to the table on which something, a square
pan, was covered by a coarse linen cloth. The cloth Theo
drew away. It was the cheesecake which Elsa had promised him.

The boy reached out his hand and gently set his palm
on the crust. It was still warm. Only now did he cry—a
single tear trickling down to his chin. When he withdrew
the hand, it was a fist.

"I, Father," said the boy, thumping his chest with his
fist, "I will heal the mind."

II

HOHENHEIM, THE APPRENTICE

There are two kinds of knowledge, that of experience and that of our own cleverness; one kind is the foundation and teacher of the physician, the other is his misleading and error. He receives the first from the fire when he plies Vulcan's tools in transmuting, forging, reducing, solving, perfecting with all the processing pertaining to such work. The other kind of knowledge is but lumber without experiment; it may prove right once, but not invariably, and it does not do to build upon such a foundation. Error is built upon it, error glossed over with sophistries. Nature in the fire of experiment shall be our teacher.

PARACELSUS

4

Gutta cavat lapidem non vi, sed saepe cadendo.

For the forty-ninth time young Theophrastus von Hohenheim, now a stocky dreamer of fourteen, was writing the Latin saw on the slate wall of a rectory basement somewhere on the outskirts of Villach, Carinthia.

He had mistranslated it upstairs in his daily lesson with Bishop Erhard of Lavanttal and the bishop, a jolly fat man who looked more at home with a leg of lamb in his hand than a Bible, had given him busy work. He was to write it over and over again with the piece of white rock until, as the bishop put it, the "tongue of fire" descended with the answer. Oh, he had pieced it all together by now: "The drop hollows out the rock not by force, but by repeated dropping." It was one of the good bishop's little sayings. But Theophrastus' mind wasn't on Latin; it seldom had been. He was trying to find a way to divert Erhard's attention from the daily grind.

"What earthly good was it anyway," he thought, "all

this Latin and Greek and rhetoric and logic? What under
heaven did Greek have to do with dysentery, besides
causing it? Could Latin cure a cold? And rhetoric—would
an ulcer shrivel up at the sound of a well-rounded phrase?
And as for logic, nobody could talk so stupidly and so long
as a self-styled logician."

The boy stole a look at his tutor. Erhard had just tipped
an earthen cup full of red wine from a giant alembic and
was tossing off an enormous mouthful with a sigh. Then,
happily flicking a few drops off the front of his habit, he
picked up some bellows and, puffing enormously himself,
began working up a flame. And watching him, the boy felt
happy too. For ever since they moved downstairs, and the
basement turned out to be a laboratory, Theophrastus was
sure that the daily grind was over. He had found the way:
Erhard was a "gold cook," and there wasn't an alchemist
alive who wouldn't rather talk of transmutations than
tenses.

With a crafty look in his eye, Theophrastus held the
piece of limestone to the window and fell into a deep study
of it.

"*Labor,*" came the powerful voice of Erhard. "*Labor omni
vincit.*" That meant "Get busy," Theophrastus was sure.
Everything the bishop said meant "Get busy."

"I was just thinking, Father . . ."

"A cause for great rejoicing!" Erhard said wryly. "Thinking what?"

"How Latin and limestone go together. How apt it is."

"*Latine, Latine,* Theophrastus," said Erhard. "Speak
Latin, think Latin, live Latin!"

The boy was crestfallen. Erhard turned back to his
bench and set an iron crucible over the glowing coals. He
hadn't risen to the bait; the ruse had failed.

With a great sigh Theophrastus looked outside through the grilled window of the basement. He could make out, one third of the way up, the movement of men on Lead Mountain; the day shift was just finishing and the "hell shift" just coming on. Villach was an exciting place, no doubt about it now, but it had taken him a long, long time to like it as much as Einsiedeln. It was that first impression.

Soon after Elsa's death Wilhelm and Theo had moved, crossing the mountains to Villach where the famous Lead and Foundry Mountains were located. The mountains supplied the whole of Europe with most of its lead, as well as a number of other metals, including gold; and they were owned entire by the House of Fugger, the merchant princes who loaned money to the emperor himself. Wilhelm would teach at the school of mining and, together with his son, would find a cure for the mysterious miner's disease.

The disease was caused by the earth creatures or gnomes who lived in the mountain. They frowned on men's meddling with their homes and their way of life. And so, always careful to stay out of sight, they harassed the miners. They caused ropes to slip, axles to snap and rocks to slide. And much worse, they cast a series of spells. The first sign a miner had that he had become their victim was that he grew very pale. Then, gradually, his appetite failed. Not only did food become uninteresting to him; it became repulsive. What food he swallowed turned into a searing hot pain in his belly and his guts.

Despite these warnings, if a miner, perhaps because he had a half-dozen children to feed, persisted in returning to the mines, the gnomes would sap his strength, bit by bit. First the outermost joints of the toes and the fingers would go; he couldn't pick up a bolt or undo a button. Then the

next joint and the next went limp and shaky, until he had
the "wrist drop." And if the spell cast was the "spell of
death," the arms all the way to the shoulder, and the legs
to the hip joint, became weak and numb and shook with
the palsy. To the lead miners of Villach death came slowly
and horribly. In the next three years, Theophrastus, with
his own eyes, was to see scores of miners die.

But anxious as he was to help Wilhelm, he had not
counted on the dingy aspect of a mining town. And so
when, after a tiring two-week ride, Wilhelm stopped their
bulging wagon on a mountain pass to give his son a first
glimse of Villach, the boy had to fight back the tears. The
town looked bad and smelled worse. Miles back they
had noticed an unsavory smell, vaguely like cooked cabbage, in the air. As they drew nearer, what passed for cabbage became more like rotten eggs, then the rotten eggs at
last became like the stench of human waste. And when Wilhelm stopped their wagon on the rainshed of the pass, Theo
saw the source of it.

A vast chunk of Lead Mountain had been gouged away,
and on the bottom lip of the hole, out of a dozen or so
squat stone ovens, thick bluish-gray billows of smoke
belched into the air. They were roasting out the sulphur.
To and from these ovens, streams of figures—men and
women and boys no older than nine—were moving the pulverized ore in mule-driven boxcars and man-driven wheel-
barrows, in wooden troughs and buckets, over trestles and
through tunnels and down wooden ramps, some of them
dumping their glistening gray loads, and others returning
for more. They looked like ants picking their way among
bonfires. And through the vast blanket of smoke, at the foot
of the mountain, lay Villach—grimy houses with steep,
leaden roofs clustered about a grimy cathedral.

A short month later, it seemed to the boy that he had never been so happy. Wilhelm had shown him how to handle the *aquas* and the alkalis, and had given him perfect freedom in the basement laboratory. And just as now, scrawling dead Latin sayings on a slate wall, he couldn't wait for Bishop Erhard to dismiss him so that he could get back to his retort. . . .

"How, apt?" Erhard's booming voice cut into his thoughts and startled him. Theophrastus blinked; his mind was adrift. "You said limestone is 'apt' for Latin. How, apt?"

He did bite after all! thought the boy. *The fish is hooked!* He felt wonderfully elated, but when he spoke he tried to keep his voice casual.

"Why," said Theophrastus, "to be writing the words of a dead language with a rock full of dead air."

The bishop didn't seem to understand at first. Then his mouth opened and his belly began to shake, but it was some time before any sound came. When it did come, it was a guffaw so powerful that it seemed to shake the beams of the floor overhead.

"*Novus homo,*" he said, wiping his eyes with his sleeve. "Upstart! Stripling, he is, with scarce a baker's dozen years upon his head, and already he has the philosophers' stone—and, mind you, one that turns stone into air. And *dead* air in the bargain!"

"Fire is life, you grant it?" said the boy.

"I grant it."

"And that which puts out life is death?"

Another spasm of laughter was coming, but Erhard managed to say, "Ach, when your Latin flies, your logic staggers. Air is the *life* of fire, how can air put it out?"

Theophrastus did not pause to answer, but walked directly to the good bishop's workbench and took it over.

Setting the piece of limestone into a crucible, he pulverized it into a white powder; this powder he carefully fret into a small alembic; and the snout of the alembic he set carefully, so that it emptied directly over the lit flame of a candle.

"*Aqua fortis?*" he asked, looking at the shelf. Already impressed with the brisk, sure movements of Theophrastus' hands, Erhard was wide-eyed; the laughter was fast draining from his face. He pointed to a small stoppered jug. The boy removed the stopper and down the side of the glass poured a thin coating of the acid; then, almost as part of the same movement, he set on the alembic's lid. On the instant of contact the powder bubbled furiously; an angry froth sprung up so quickly it made the bishop flinch. Then, as the seething leveled off, both turned their eyes to the flame of the candle. For a full minute, nothing happened, and then, as the boiling continued inside unabated, the flame suddenly retreated back onto its wick. It dwindled and went out, without so much as a trail of smoke.

"*Mirabile visu!*" said Erhard. "A marvel, a genuine marvel!" He tipped the giant alembic full of wine again, this time filling two of the earthen cups, and offered one to Theophrastus. He looked a long time at the boy, as if seeing him for the first time. "An excellent trick, I own it," he said. "But still, a trick. *Lusus naturae,* neither more nor less." He tossed back his head, opened his mouth and dumped the whole cupful of wine into the gaping maw. He stood so, not swallowing, but letting the wine find its own way into his gullet. Then leaning forward, he said in a voice grave and confidential:

"Tomorrow I will show you something, boy. And I don't mean one of your little tricks. Tomorrow I will show you *alchemy!*"

Later that evening, as Theophrastus opened the door to his house, the smell of roast goose filled his nostrils. When Hans, their housekeeper, cooked goose in the middle of the week, it meant one thing: there was a guest for supper.

"Who's coming, Hans?" he said on the way to the leaden washbowl.

"Not coming, Master Theo. Here!" said Hans, pointing down to indicate that Wilhelm and the guest were in the laboratory downstairs.

"So who?" demanded the boy. Hans, he knew, was in one of his high moods, and he braced himself. The stumpy, gnomelike Hans had only two moods; he was either aggressively happy or aggressively grumpy, and Theophrastus frankly preferred the grumpy variety. For when he was happy, Hans was chock-full of jokes which were so bad that they often made the boy moan. Theophrastus was wiping the sting of the alkaline soapsuds out of his eyes when he heard Hans' voice in his ear:

"The Holy Ghost. The Holy Ghost is coming!" And with a peal of laughter at his own humor, Hans pranced back into his kitchen.

Theophrastus tried to snort his disgust but he heard himself laughing instead. He couldn't be angry with Hans for long. Much as he suffered from the bad jokes, he always remembered Hans as he was that first day, and it soothed the anger away.

Three years back Theophrastus had answered an urgent knock at the door to find Wilhelm helping a man, who was more than half dead, keep on his feet. It was the top foreman of the Fugger mines—Hans. The face of death showed through his features; his skin was pale, almost bluish, and was pulled tightly over the bones; the mouth and nostrils were slavering; the hands were quivering and limp. Only a fierce, deep glow in the eyes was alive. Theophrastus had tried to give him a hand, but the stubborn miner insisted on going it alone. Steadying himself along the wall, he worked his way in, consciously and with great effort setting one leg ahead of the other toward a chair. He had almost made it, when both knees buckled at once; toppling, he fell, the length of his body thumping the floor. Yet even then he accepted no help.

He worked himself to his hands and knees and, hooking his powerful forearms over the arms of the chair, he hoisted himself high enough to maneuver himself into a sitting position. Panting and triumphant he had gasped, "Hans—he don't make trouble. . . ." And the look in his eyes, the self-possessed and unyielding sanity, was the first clue, unconscious as yet, to Theophrastus' understanding of the mind. Years later he was to remember that look, when he came to realize that patients with such a look could forestall death itself for a time.

"I'm going to make you jester to the king, you know it, Hans?" said Theophrastus, still laughing.

The compliment made Hans even merrier. He was carrying a rose-tinted tumbler in either hand, and as he moved toward the table he broke into a jig. He ended, placing the tumblers on the fresh linen with a flourish, and spoke.

"Herr Fugger, no less. It is my old boss what is downstairs right now!"

The boy was thunderstruck. "The owner of the mountains, the banker for the emperor, he's here?"

"Here!"

"Why?"

"Why should a man come to a doctor's house. To see of course the doctor."

He's ill, then?" Theophrastus was caught off guard.

"Oh *ja*, he's ill, Herr Fugger. He's very ill," Hans said, suddenly coy. The tone of his voice told Theophrastus that another joke was coming, but it was too late to stop it. "His back is broke," said Hans, straining to be solemn.

"All right, all right, Hans. Why 'his back is broke'?"

Hans, already whinnying with anticipation, said, "From carrying all his gold from bank to bank." He stomped and whooped, almost suffocating himself with laughter as he made his way back into the kitchen. As soon as his reason returned, he rang the big cowbell which announced supper.

A long-suffering smile on his face, Theophrastus watched Hans move into the kitchen. And suddenly as he watched, it occurred to him why Herr Fugger had come. Hans was a test case in Wilhelm's search for a cure to the "incurable" miner's disease—and Hans was well. He had traveled the long road back almost from death itself and was now a model of health, not only of body but of mind. Diet, sunlight, exercise—and above all, a vacation from the dust of the mines and the fumes of the roasting ovens—had turned the trick.

Hundreds of miners now afflicted could be cured and countless thousands to come could be spared simply by rotating jobs, by alternating for a planting or a harvest on one of the Fugger farms. The plan no doubt entailed a little inefficiency; it would cut into the profits. But it would make for a far healthier community, not to mention an easier conscience for the Fugger family.

But when Wilhelm appeared with Herr Fugger, it was

clear that the powerful merchant had rejected Wilhelm's plan. Between host and guest there was a decided coolness. Their dialogue was formal and strained.

"A three-month change per year, Herr Fugger," Wilhelm was saying. "It would save their lives."

The merchant smiled urbanely. "It is hard, steady work that saves the soul."

"And puts the gold into your moneybags," said Theophrastus heatedly, cutting in.

"Theo . . . !" said a surprised Wilhelm as the merchant prince, with an arched eyebrow, turned to the boy. "And food into their mouths, young man," he said. "Into the bellies of their children."

"Ah, yes," said Theophrastus, his eyes blazing. "With the one hand you feed them . . . !"

"You will control your mouth, young man," said the boy's father.

"Let the boy speak. He simply states his father's thoughts unveiled," said Herr Fugger, amused. "And with the other hand, I . . . ?"

"Let them die. You murder them!"

Wilhelm was beside himself with anger. "You dare speak to a guest in such a manner? I can't believe, I can't permit it! Out with you, out!"

"Permit, Papa?" There were tears in the boy's eyes. "And how can you permit hundreds of men to die. You are their doctor, you are the one who knows!" The first rift had come between father and son. Theophrastus turned blindly and ran out, slamming the door behind him. Until his disappointment and his anger had worn away, he walked about unaware for a long while, and slept outside under the stars.

He would have run away except, for the first time he could remember, he wanted to attend his class. He couldn't wait to see the "alchemy" which the bishop promised. He opened the rectory door and found a note on the desk: *"Venite in infernis."* He was to join Erhard downstairs, "in hell." There, an astonishing sight greeted his eyes.

Overnight the laboratory had doubled in size. Two walls, including the slate slab with his forty-nine Latin saws, were panels; they had been slid into the earth. In the new room on the right, Erhard was fussing about a distiller, a cylindrical oven of stone with a huge, inverted funnel at the top. Trickling down a tube leading from this funnel into a double-eared jug, or "pelican," was quicksilver, and another pelican, brimful, was sitting alongside.

In the other new room straight ahead was an alchemical oven, or "athanor," of a radically new kind. It was specially designed and constructed, pieces of sheet metal fitted together so that, fire pit, door and slabs, it looked like the decapitated head of a fiend. Out of its head rose a serrated rod suggesting a giant piston inside, next to an escape valve which was already hissing steam. Quite a sight, thought the boy; how secretly, how slyly had jolly old Erhard transformed the rectory wine cellar into a laboratory, no doubt enjoining his workmen to secrecy on pain of damnation and hell-fire!

"Come in, my son, come in! That innocent mouthful there is yours." Mopping his neck with a perfumed handkerchief, he drained his own cupful of wine; then, as he tipped himself another, he turned a practiced eye across the room to the athanor. It needed more fuel.

"Ach," he said, "food, food for Beelzebub!" Slue-footed and puffing, he shuffled over to the furnace and picked up a shovel. Making a herculean effort, he tossed in two shovelfuls of coal. But the effort was too great. He straightened up, blowing furiously, and turned a baleful eye upon the boy. Theophrastus took the hint. He relieved the fat man of the shovel, tossed in several more, and pushed shut the mouth of "Beelzebub."

But all of a sudden, the boy found himself doing all the dirty work. He was tending both distiller and athanor as the bishop, sitting on the bench next to the wine, was giving him a lesson in "applied logic"—on the subject of gold. He asked Theophrastus, between shovelfuls, to go over to the window and look out.

"What do you see?" he said.

Beyond the grilling, a big black cloud with white rounded edges was racing past the blunted peak of Lead Mountain.

"Lead Mountain," the boy said.

"Gold Mountain. You see 'Gold Mountain,' boy," Erhard said. Delighted at Theophrastus' bewilderment Erhard, so full of his subject that an unearthly glint crept into his eyes, went on to explain how all earth, and especially all metals, "grow." So magnificent is God's earth, he said, that everything in and of it aspires to become something higher. Among the metals, those which are "base" evolve into those which are "noble." The metals, astrologically, proceed from the lead of the outermost planet, Saturn, moving inwardly from planet to planet until they have reached the gold of the sun. Thus, lead aspires to the tin of Jupiter, tin to the iron of Mars, to the copper of Venus, to the quicksilver of Mercury, thence into the golden sun.

Erhard paused now, and leaned forward. He even set aside his cup. "Now, boy," he said, "give me both ears and all your brain." Both pelicans at the distiller were full and Erhard motioned him to take them over to the athanor.

Looping a finger through the "ears," he tried lifting them both at once and was stunned to find them heavy. The weight of one almost staggered him.

"Herr Fugger, boy," said Erhard gravely, "what metals does he mine?"

"Well . . . lead." Theophrastus eased the jug down and mopped his brow. "Some iron, some copper. A little silver . . ." His voice trailed off as he heard himself say, "Small traces of *gold!*" Erhard saw by the look in his eye that the "tongue of fire" had again descended upon Theophrastus.

"She's a young mountain, boy, she needs a small millennium to ripen. But give her time enough, Lead Mountain and all the metals in her will be gold!"

"A millennium . . . is . . ." The boy was looking for the flaw.

". . . is a long, long time. Exactly." Erhard slid off the bench onto his feet as the boy carried over the second pelican of quicksilver to the furnace. "Given:" said Erhard, the master logician now, "that metals grow to gold. Desired: to speed millennium into an hour. Required: the means, the *modus operandi.* You with me, boy?"

"I'm with you, Father."

"Let's look at it again."

The two of them went over to the window. They looked out and up. Never had the mutilated mountain seemed so mysterious.

"What does she have, our mountain?" said Erhard, putting an arm around the boy's shoulders. His voice was trembling with rapture. "She has time. But man—Erhard, and even Theophrastus, our time is of another world, eh boy? So: time she has. What other does she have . . . ?"

"Heat!" said the boy, with growing excitement.

"And so, the athanor. Yet heat is not enough. For every metal cook since Vulcan has had heat. What other does she have that man, until this day, has lacked?"

Theophrastus was stumped.

"Where do we mine the ore?" The bishop was irritated.

"Out of her side."

"Of course, out of her side. But how far *up*?"

"Maybe one third . . ."

"In other words," Erhard said triumphantly, "there's two thirds of the mountain weighing *down!*"

"Pressure," said the boy in a hoarse whisper.

"Pres-sure!" said the bishop with the same gesture he used at Mass during the consecration of the wafer. "The alchemist before the millennium, because he has no time, must have the pressure!"

A blast which quickly turned into a steady screech reverberated through the laboratory. It was the steam valve. The moment of truth had come!

Erhard sprang into action with such energy that his very body seemed to have grown younger. He lifted open the door, the "nose" of Beelzebub, which was fixed on the hinge side with four bolts. Out of this opening, with tongs, he drew a long bread pan and into it poured the contents of both pelicans. This pan he then slid into place and closed the door, in the same motion stopping the escape valve by screwing down a tiny wheel. Immediately the serrated rod went down the space of a tooth, making a distinct click.

And now it was clear to the boy that the rod could go down but, being trapped by a flap hinge atop the athanor, could not reascend. In fact, the whole plan of the athanor came to him: the water boiling inside was making steam; the steam was creating pressure; the pressure was pushing down a huge piston whose rod, tooth by tooth, was mechanically locked into place by the hinge; and a combination of great pressure from above and great heat from below would, after a sudden cooling perhaps, transform the pan of mercury into an ingot of pure gold! Theophrastus was beside himself with excitement.

Both laid on the coals; Theophrastus wielded the shovel, and Erhard, careful not to get his fingers dirty, tossed in a token chunk or two. Down went the piston, click after click, with each click a little slower, a little more reluctant. Bishop and boy sweated profusely. The rod had gone down a full meter and only two teeth were showing, when it started to shudder.

"More coal, Master Erhard?" asked the boy.

"Maybe one . . . more," said the bishop, but he was none too sure. Theophrastus tossed on another shovelful. The flames crackled and roared, and the rod now began to wobble wildly although, hair by hair, it continued working its way downward.

Again it clicked. There was only one to go. Their eyes were fixed on the rod which no longer seemed to move. The boy looked to the bishop.

"Maybe a half," he said. "Maybe a little half." He spoke very low, for fear of disturbing some mysterious balance.

But before Theophrastus could add the last shovelful, the piston rod stopped its wobbling with a dramatic suddenness. In the intense quiet came a new sound, something between a ringing and a hiss. The smell of scorched metal was very strong.

"Click!" The piston was now compressed to the full.

"*Gloria in excelsis Deo!*" whispered Erhard, making the sign of the cross. He started to bless Beelzebub but, noticing that his hand was empty he danced, on tiptoe, over to the wine. He wasn't bothering with any cup, not now. "Wine and gold, wine and gold!" he chanted, and lifting the alembic high over his upturned mouth, he let it flow first into the gaping hole and then overflow onto his face and hair. Erhard was setting the alembic, tenderly almost, on the workbench when Theophrastus heard a tiny but distinct "ping" behind him.

Something small and solid struck the stone wall directly in front of the athanor. It ricocheted into the coalbin. Both froze, listening intently.

"Ping!"

Theophrastus had scarcely located the source of this second sound—the "nose" of Beelzebub which closed in the precious pan of metal—when before his eyes the entire door, with a "chuff!" detached itself and, spinning wildly, clattered against the wall where the first "ping" had hit. Immediately, a silvery vapor like a lazy snake climbed through the opening.

In a matter of seconds Erhard was halfway up the stairs. For a fat man, his movements were remarkable. "*Currite*, Theophrastus!" he shouted over his shoulder. "Run for your life!"

Theophrastus did not wait to hear it twice. He had already taken a few steps when, *varrooom!* A blast came from behind him, knocking him to the floor. As he rolled over trying to find his legs, he caught a glance of a gaping hole, crescent-shaped, where the top of the athanor had been torn upward by the piston. Around the bent rod rose the pearly and poisonous billows of mercury vapor and steam.

It was the last he saw that day of the bishop's basement. The next thing he remembered afterward, was standing outside in the yard and shouting to Erhard, who had taken the notion to dart into the doomed wine cellar. In a few very long seconds, Erhard reappeared at the doorway, the alembic of wine pressed into the folds of his bare belly.

"My wines," he moaned as he stroked the side of the alembic. "My wines are ruined. Except of course," he added with a rueful grin, "this tiny mouthful for tomorrow's Mass."

There was nothing to say. The two stood in glum silence watching the vapors ooze out of the foundations of the house. Theophrastus spoke first.

"Next time, maybe . . . some bigger bolts . . . ?"

"No next time, boy." Erhard shook his grizzled head. "You see white smoke out of a basement. I see handwriting on the wall." He searched for the Latin saw which would cover the occasion and found it. "*Semel abbas, semper abbas*," he pronounced. "Once an abbot, always an abbot, eh boy?" he translated, with a great laugh.

A horse whinnied behind them. It was Wilhelm, mounted, with an extra horse in tow. He was on the way to help with the breech delivery of a calf. He could use help if the boy were of a mind.

The boy was. At the sight of his father, a surge of gladness warmed his chest. He hadn't changed his mind about the duty of a doctor, not a bit; but perhaps his father's truth was not his own. In any case, it didn't matter. He rode out to the new calf with a subtle new relation between Wilhelm and himself. He had come to know a little more who he was. "What great good fortune," he thought, "not only to have such a father, but to have jolly, fat Erhard for a tutor—one who believed in applying rhetoric and logic, Greek and Latin, to the study of metals."

5

S AYING GOOD-BY to Wilhelm wasn't easy.

As the gnomelike Hans, who had adopted a brusque manner to hide his feelings, bustled in and out of the house loading clothes and books and a leather satchel full of virtues onto the gray mare, young Hohenheim and his father, standing on the stone porch, were having a farewell chat.

"These things we do with minerals," Wilhelm was saying, "with salts and *aquas* . . . at Tübingen, they won't go well."

"It is not my job to hide the truth," said Theophrastus.

"Learn what they have to teach. Get your degree." Wilhelm smiled wryly. "With a degree it's easier to change the world."

Theophrastus did not return the smile; and looking at his son, Wilhelm wondered what word or combination of words might make his way easier. He knew that the boy, who at fifteen seemed to have passed from youth to manhood without the awkward stage between, had a keen mind and an open heart; but he knew too, to his pride and fear, that Theophrastus had something else that set him apart. He had a consuming and disturbing drive toward something which made him incapable of laughing away a lie. The boy took his truth very personally. He identified himself with it.

"Weigh everything with patience, hear me, Theo?" said Wilhelm.

The mare was ready, and Hans, blinking back a tear, stood holding her reins. Expertly, Theophrastus fixed his foot into the stirrup, swung up and on, and took the reins.

"The school's no worse than most," Wilhelm called up. And Theophrastus, looking down at his father's face, was shocked to find it suddenly aged. There was so much gray in the hair, so many lines around the eyes. There was the leaden pallor of the skin. But there was also that wonderfully warm smile. He swallowed hard.

"It's your school, Papa. It must be better," he said.

Wilhelm was pleased. "It's no doubt changing for the better," he said. He opened his arms expansively. "The world, boy, the entire world is changing every day. A dozen printing presses across the country. Dozens of new routes to the New World, to the East. New fabrics, spices, medicines. The world you're riding into, it's alive. It's waking up to monsters and to marvels." Wilhelm stopped abruptly and lowered his voice. "Up north in Poland, Theo, there's this canon. Nicholas Koppernigk. He wants to change the motions of the heavens."

Impatient to go, the mare sidled out into the street and Theophrastus clucked her back to the curb.

"How, change?" he said, curious.

"He writes—without the Church's blessing, on the sly—

the earth is just another wanderer. The sun stands still."

This piece of gossip they both found enormously funny, probably because they needed release from the clumsiness of saying good-by. But when Theophrastus stopped laughing, he was looking intently up at the white disc behind the sulphurous pall; and again, Wilhelm was pleased.

"Good, boy, good," he said. "Weigh everything with patience." He slapped the rump of the mare and, with a lurch, Theophrastus was off to Tübingen University. Halfway down the block, he turned in his saddle and saw his father still there, on the stone porch, watching. It was not until he was in open country outside Villach that he noticed the weight in the pocket of his leather alchemist's jacket. It was a moneybag full of gold Florentine ducats and a note with two addresses, in Wilhelm's hand: "Friedrich Bauern & Frieda/King's Street in Tübingen/By the Medici Pawnshop three houses down" and "Joachim von Waadt called Vadianus/University of Vienna/Rector." Under the addresses were the words, "These men of peace can soothe a student's anger." It was signed formally: "Wilhelm von Hohenheim, Doctor of Medicine." And under his signature, this postscript: "Come back a doctor. Not before."

His sight, a week later, of the southeast gate of Tübingen made Theophrastus uneasy. There was the curious babble coming from inside the walls. And outside the walls, to either side of the gate, like long, black ropes frayed at the top, three columns of smoke were rising through the cold morning air. It was a sure sign of plague.

The columns of smoke were no mystery to him. To prevent contagion, all the personal property of plague victims was condemned. "Death teams" wearing linen masks, and

using long poles, loaded clothes and bedding, furniture
and drapes onto oxcarts; they walked their animals outside
the walls and put their loads to the torch. Yet once aflame,
these piles would often be scattered by gypsies and riffraff
and abandoned waifs. At the pile nearest the gate, Theophrastus could see a grizzled old man with one leg, probably a veteran of the war with the Turks, poking around
with his crutch.

His fear that he might be turned away proved to be
unfounded. Cases of plague at Tübingen that year were
evidently isolated and few. The gate was open; and from
his cubicle a sleepy guard blinked at Theophrastus and,
without getting to his feet, waved him in with his spear.

"Soo-ey!"

Inside the walls, he could clearly hear the curious babble coming from several sections of the city. He heard the
sound again: "Soo-soo-soo-ey!" and said aloud, "Hogs!"
It sounded for all the world like peasants calling hogs.
And sure enough, looking down the first cross street, he
saw two men driving before them a dozen grunting and
snorting hogs. The street was unbelievably littered.

Hogs, it turned out, were the Town Council's answer to
the sewage and garbage problem. Ever since the *Bund-
schuh* uprising some half-dozen years before, the peasants
from the outlying farms, who had collected the wastes for
fertilizer, had refused to co-operate. They saw little point
in trying to produce bumper harvests; for what their lords
and the Church did not take, the various professionals from
doctor to huckster did, and such passive resistance as
abandoning city wastes was the least they could do. But
the city fathers of Tübingen were a shrewd and resource-
ful lot; and when one of them returned from Italy, the

culture center of Europe, with a new approach to this problem, they decided to give it a try.

A dozen hogs were assigned to each of several slum sectors. The burgers were instructed first thing in the morning to dump their night pots and their garbage at designated spots on the streets. And at this hour a pair of swineherds, under city pay, drove their charges down the streets. Except for the giant rats which openly vied with the hogs for the refuse, and the hordes of insects which swarmed over the city in clement weather, the new system was working extremely well. The burgers were happy because they no longer had to dig the deep holes or live with putrid odors, and the tax-minded city fathers were gleeful because the hogs, which fattened very quickly on this rich fare, brought in an unexpected source of revenue.

Near the university grounds the air was more pleasant, but it wasn't a bit more quiet. Blocks away he heard a hubbub, and as he turned the last corner he saw throngs of students, hundreds of them, facing a raised wooden dais in the center of the quadrangle. On this stage two black-gowned professors were "debating," except that the debate had reached a stage where the two were directing their comments at each other with closed fists. One of these worthies would shout an angry sentence to the other, as half of the audience, all of whom wore wide-brimmed hats with a single white chicken feather attached, would cheer; and as the second delivered his retort the other half of the audience, these wearing brown arm bands on their sleeves, would answer with a cheer of their own. In the air between the two groups was a continual rain of missiles.

As Theophrastus surveyed this scene, he saw a young fellow with a white chicken feather in his hat come bustling through the stone gate. Theophrastus asked him the subject of the debate.

The fellow, a skinny, surly chap with pimples all over his face, glared up at Theophrastus. He shot his forefinger into the air and exclaimed, "It's war, friend. War!" Then, taking a step toward the horse, he said, almost accusingly, "Are you a Wing or a Clod?" But before Theophrastus could speak, he answered his own question.

"You're neither. You're new here," he said. "Come with me." And he bolted across the cobblestones to a tavern.

The young man took himself so seriously that Theophrastus had to laugh. He dismounted, looped the reins of the mare in the ring of a hitching post and crossed the street. He had to run to catch up.

The young man, a Hungarian named Gregor, was so excited by the debate that he had forgotten—or so he said—to eat for three days. No sooner had he entered the door than he called out his order for yellow cheese and barley beer. He plopped down at the nearest table, sat up rigidly; and then, reverently, he removed the chicken feather from his hat and set it, as if it were a sacrament, on the table between them.

"I am a Wing," he said.

Theophrastus dared to ask: "What does it mean, to be a 'Wing' or a 'Clod'?"

"The Clods are heretics, they're devils. They are the ruination of the world." And again the forefinger shot into the air.

Theophrastus had hoped that the debate was either on some medical subject or about the authenticity of another manuscript "find." He showed his disappointment.

"You're not debating medicine?" he said.

"Of course we are," began Gregor, as if outraged. But

at this point a fat, yawning maid dumped the cheese and the barley beer onto the table. Gregor bit off a huge chunk of cheese and resumed his explanation talking through a yellow blob: "We are debating *knowledge*," he said.

He chewed and drank and coughed and drank again. Then he went on.

"You think you are a scholar, eh? You're not. You," he said, pointing the cheese at Theophrastus' nose, "you are a soldier in a *war!* You best choose right." He had actually put the last corner of cheese into his mouth when he withdrew it and said, "You're fighting a battle. The most important since the sack of Rome!" And then a fit of perfect silence descended on him.

Theophrastus didn't really want to break this silence, but he couldn't help it. "What battle?" he asked.

"*De flatus vocis*," said Gregor. The forefinger, cheese and all, flew up toward the heavens. "The Battle of the Puff of Air."

As Theophrastus guessed, it was not a battle which excited him. He didn't want to know about the war, but he did want to know more about Gregor. Gregor was a study. There was a ring of beer froth on his sparse mustache and, delicately, he reached up the end of his cape and patted it away. Then, leaning halfway across the table he solemnly tapped Theophrastus' chest with the cheese. He was going to say something very, very important.

"How do you know?" he said.

"How do I know what?" said Theophrastus.

"How do you know what you know? How do you know anything? That's what this war is all about!" In a single motion, he finished his cheese and tossed off his beer. Then, speaking very rapidly, and yet with surprising point, he gave Theophrastus a clear picture of the battle.

A baby learning to talk and to think, explained Gregor, sees a red shoe. Then he sees a red bird, a red glass, a red rose. At some point along the way, he knows that "red" is not a thing but a thought, he picks up the idea of "redness." From many particular things, or "singulars," he has learned "redness," a "universal."

Now, both camps, Wings and Clods, were agreed that the man who was truly educated, who attained to genius and to sainthood, was simply the one whose brain moved most comfortably among the greatest number of these "universals," who in fact had passed from the ideas of things less and less concrete, from "tree" to "cloud" to "light," to the ideas of things more and more abstract, say, from "motion" to "number" to "soul." The Battle of the Puff of Air was about the nature of these universals. Did they, as the Platonist Wings said, come from and belong to the soul and therefore could not be destroyed, even by death? Or were they—as the Aristotelian Clods corrupted by recent thinkers, maintained—only a "puff of air" which stopped existing the minute they left the mind in thought or the mouth in speech?

Theophrastus couldn't believe his ears. *This* was the bone of contention? Grown men were arguing about *this?* Sitting across from Gregor that day, the thought first came to Theophrastus that like Gregor, the world of medicine was slightly insane.

A few weeks later he came across the leader of the Clods sitting on a bench, staring abstractedly off at a cloud. The man, he knew, was Herr Professor Georg Zeugg, head of the school of medicine. Theophrastus, who was not much with the social graces, came straight to the point.

"If universals are a puff of air," he blurted, "how does this heal the sick?"

A look of extreme irritation crossed the professor's face. This boy had just ruptured one of his universals.

"That pitfall I avoided years ago," he said, shifting his position. Then he added sarcastically, "About your age."

"Perhaps I can avoid it too," murmured Theophrastus. He hadn't meant to offend.

Professor Zeugg sat up. He appreciated anyone who made a show of humility before his greatness. The irritation on his face was replaced by a look of cleverness.

"The mind's an instrument of truth, you see, boy? But if the instrument is infirm, then what is truth? What good to diagnose, prescribe? We only meddle with God's will. If the mind's infirm, what can we do?"

"We can stop thinking," said Theophrastus passionately. The professor, thinking the boy had become a wit, started to laugh, but on second glance saw that he was perfectly sincere.

"What can you believe, if not your mind," he asked. He was sure the boy was driven into a corner.

"I can believe my eyes, my ears, my nose . . . !" said Theophrastus.

Professor Zeugg glared at him a moment. Then he sank back into his seat. "Switzers!" he said, with contempt. "Medicine is not for Switzers, boy. Better for you, a monk." His eyes looked off and found the cloud again. The interview was clearly at an end.

Theophrastus had taken a dozen steps away, when he heard the professor call after him:

"For you, Franciscan," he said.

It was high time to seek out one of the men of peace on Wilhelm's card.

King Street, where Friedrich Bauern lived, was among those cleaned by hogs. Theophrastus picked his way over the litter and, finding the sign of the three balls, counted three doors down from the pawn shop. The door, over a rise of three steps, was padlocked, and the single window was boarded over with a double X. The Bauerns were victims of the plague.

His father would want details; he looked around for the guard on duty. None was in sight. He was about to leave when he heard a voice, a woman scolding, coming from inside. Peering through the window, he saw a two-year-old boy sitting on the floor. By city ordinance, all occupants of a stricken house were locked in. He had known of the practice, but now that it affected him personally, Theophrastus was horrified. He ran up the stairs to the door—it had a huge red X scrawled across it—and shook the padlock.

The door of the inn across the street burst open and a guard, stuffing his shirttail into his trousers, came running out.

"What are you, blind or crazy? Come down from there, it's the pest!"

"I am a student of medicine. These are my friends."

"I don't care if they're friends of the Pope himself. I got my orders." He slurred these words and, standing there now, was a bit shaky on his feet.

"Drinking on duty, is that in your orders?" asked Theophrastus pointedly.

The guard glared at him stupidly but after a second's consideration, plodded up the stairs and turned the key. "What kind of crazy fool would ask for the plague?" he mumbled.

Theophrastus took the padlock with him and pushed open the door. The floor on the far side of the huge room was alive with rats. They scrambled and scratched and cheeped, some of them literally climbing over others to get to a fallen body near the fireplace, to the corpse of Friedrich Bauern. They took not the slightest notice of Theophrastus' presence.

On the table a few feet back from the window were two more bodies, of children, neatly laid out; there, Frieda Bauern kept knocking one rat after another off the table with a piece of kindling, all the while scolding them. "Stupid," she mumbled, mesmerized, "stupid, stupid," and struck the fat belly of a rat which fell with a squeak as another took its place. It was only the little boy who noticed him. Seeing the door open, he struggled to his feet with a thin, dry wail. He was hungry and, above all, thirsty; but it was at once clear to Theophrastus that, with some food and drink, the child was perfectly healthy.

In a wave of disgust for the rats, Theophrastus removed his leather jacket and flailed away on all sides. For a few swats they simply gave ground and went about their grisly business. And then, as at a signal, an alarm spread over them and they all, every last one of them, disappeared. They seemed to Theophrastus to have melted into the walls.

Frieda, noticing that she had nothing to strike, looked up wide eyed, with a seraphic smile on her face. Gently,

Theophrastus removed the kindling from her hand and set her down on a chair. He picked up the boy and set him on her lap. And in a minute Frieda was swaying and humming, happy and quite mad, with her son on her lap. Then Theophrastus moved over to the body of Friedrich Bauern to observe the symptoms.

It was more than he bargained for. A hot lump of nausea rose from the pit of his stomach, but it passed. His first thought was one of amazement: why hadn't so many rats eaten up the body in a minute? They had exposed the entire corpse, had gnawed away some five layers of clothing. Leaning over, he pressed his forefinger to the belly. They could not chew the flesh; it was hard as a rock. His next observation he made aloud. "The Black Death!" he said and thought, "How aptly is it named!"

Everywhere he looked, the body seemed to be black or blackening. Particularly black were the parts which normally would tend to be moist—the armpits and the crotch, the back of the knees and the ears. The sockets of the eyes were completely black, "charred" was the word which came to him. A thick, stringy fluid, like molasses, flowed out of them. And through the parted, ashen lips, he could see the black stub of a tongue. It seemed for all the world that the body was turning into charcoal.

He sank to one knee in order to take a close look at the skin. In the blackest parts he could make out hundreds of tiny eruptions, like volcanoes. These, he knew, were the buboes from which the word "bubonic" came. The least darkened skin had no buboes at all; instead, it was covered with tiny red dots. He noted the transition from the dots to the buboes and traced the history of the eruptions: they began with the point; these surrounded themselves with dozens of blisters; and around these blisters, as they grew, appeared a large outer ring, the rim of the volcano. The disease, he noted, was one of elimination, the body trying to cast off its internal poisons.

Was Frieda contaminated? He went over to her and lifted up the sleeve, exposing the joint inside the elbow. There were a dozen fiery points. Death for Frieda was now just a matter of time. And horrible as it was, he thought, it might be a blessing for her. Not so, the boy. He examined the boy thoroughly; there was no spot on him. He was thirsty and hungry and besmirched with his own dung. But he was whole.

Gently he lifted the boy out of Frieda's arms; he must take the boy away. She took no note. Moving to the door he thought happily that he was about to save his first life as a physician. He dropped the lock on the first step and turned to find the guard, more surly than ever, leveling his spear at him.

"The boy will stay," said the guard.

"The boy is whole, he is not touched by the plague."

"I got my orders."

"He'll die of thirst. He'll starve," pleaded Theophrastus.

"I got my orders," said the guard. "Go tell my chief."

There was no time to lose. Theophrastus put the boy inside the door and, mounting the mare, galloped away to the city prison.

The chief constable, when at last he was free to see this impudent scholar, referred him to the burgomeister; the burgomeister could not act without the City Council's approval. But, as Theophrastus insisted, he said that if the city physician, who was Professor Zeugg, gave his approval, he, the burgomeister would not stand in the way. After a day of waiting, Professor Zeugg interrupted a disquisition he was writing, to scrawl a note. It was on the fourth day after his visit that Theophrastus re-entered the doomed house.

Inside, he found only three bodies. Of Frieda and the boy, he found only the scattered bones.

After that, his studies weren't the same. Until now, he had felt a secret pride in mentioning to strangers that he was studying medicine; now what he felt was a shame and a growing sense of outrage. Out of respect for his father, he continued to attend classes, but his heart wasn't in it. Again and again a glimmer of hope that he was about to learn something of use in healing would rise, only to be snuffed out.

There was the series of lectures in which Professor Zeugg, the King of the Clods, was going to determine, once and for all, the cause of plague by applying his "theory of universals." In his first lecture, which outlined his approach, he noted that plague was not one of "singulars," i.e., that it did not occur in isolated individuals, but was a "universal," i.e., it occurred in epidemics. It followed, therefore, that the cause must likewise be "universal" in nature, that in fact it must be one of the four elements—fire, air, water or earth—which was decaying all over Europe. He hinted that unless this decay was checked, the end of the world was in sight.

Decayed fire took the form of "moon fever," the professor said, "and moon fever could be avoided only if every citizen were forced by law to wear wide-brimmed hats by night." Decayed air he called "pestilential spirits" which, entering the lungs, bred sickly thoughts and diseased vapors. This called for the wearing of linen masks dipped in vinegar. Decayed water came from rains contaminated by pestilential air; it could be purified by boiling and blessing. Decayed earth resulted in blighted grain, especially of the rye used in black bread. He would investigate blighted rye in detail in his second lecture.

But the second lecture had scarcely begun, with the professor comparing the stomach to a butter churn, when a star pupil posed a question out of St. Thomas Aquinas. The new routes around Africa to the East were populated by cannibals, and several crews, landing for water, had disappeared. His question combined the ideas of digestion and the resurrection of the body: in what form would the body of a Christian sailor, eaten by several cannibals, resurrect—as many parts, or as a whole? Would there be some sort of purgatorial marriage between the cannibal and the sailor? And wouldn't a cannibal who had eaten the entire body of a good Christian man, even of a saint, have the advantage on Judgment Day?

The answers to these questions Theophrastus did not stay to hear. He decided to try the teaching of Herr Professor Ludwig Schwatz, the King of the Wings. But there, as he had already guessed, he fared no better.

Professor Schwatz, a bulldog of a man with bushy eyebrows, conducted his classes with a stick. He was a master of the works of Avicenna, a colorful Persian who lived some five hundred years before, and of Celsus, a Roman patrician whose manuscript was the latest "find." He would beat the stick on the lectern to the rhythm of the phrases as the students gave back, by rote, the passage for which he had asked.

Of Avicenna, Theophrastus already had formed an opinion. It was his works which Wilhelm called, *The Doctor's Joke Book*. Avicenna, perhaps in order to give his own pupils a sense of order about the organs of the body, would put to them questions like, "Why aren't the female breasts located on the belly?" The professor did not encourage questions; and when Theophrastus exceeded what he called "the bounds of piety," Professor Schwatz sternly informed him that all knowledge, particularly in the divine art of healing, had been discovered, and it was not a student's place to question but, humbly, to learn.

It was shortly afterward, when Professor Schwatz was doling out the *De Re Medica* of Aulus Cornelius Celsus line by line that Theophrastus stopped the class. Celsus had mentioned that an herb should be classed among the diuretics, which induced urination.

"No, no," said Theophrastus aloud. "It doesn't work."

It was a change in the monotony of the class and, suddenly, everyone was listening.

"What doesn't 'work'?" said the professor, his cheeks already puffing with anger.

"The herb. My father Wilhelm tried it a dozen times. It doesn't work." Theophrastus, no whit abashed, simply stated the fact.

"Behold, young doctors," said the King of the Wings huffily. "We muzzle Celsus to hear 'para' Celsus." "Para" meant "beyond." The "young doctors" took up the phrase to laugh "Para-celsus" down. Theophrastus sat still a moment, stunned; then he got up and, as his fellow students jeered him with his new name, he walked out of the class.

He felt absolutely sure that there was nothing more for him in Tübingen. As he walked away, forlorn, he put his hand in the pocket of his leather jacket and felt his father's card. Friedrich Bauern was dead of the plague, but there was still Joachim von Waadt in Vienna.

It was time to use the other name.

6

HIS NEW NAME reached Vienna before he did.
Before "Vadianus"—that was the second name
on Wilhelm's note—became rector of the University of
Vienna, he had been Wilhelm's friend, Joachim von Waadt.
The Latin nickname was a common practice among in-
tellectuals of the day. Once they received a degree, they
assumed a Latin or Greek name which better suited their
"reborn" selves somehow bestowed upon them with the
diploma and the kiss. But Theophrastus, like his father,
thought of Vadianus as "The Bull." His body, though of
average height, was solid and square, it exuded a raw
force; and his face, with its beetling eyebrows, its wide
nostrils and sour mouth, gave him a decided no-nonsense
air. Vadianus was not an easy man to approach.

"Where is Master Vadianus' study?" Theophrastus had
interrupted a small, stocky man who was sweeping the hall
floor of the main campus building.

The man, dressed in the ballooning britches and wooden

shoes of a peasant, did not answer. He looked up at Theophrastus as though expecting a delightful surprise; and after a searching glance, he grinned as though he had found it. From the leather pouch hanging at his side, he drew a sprig of fresh mint leaves and, offering it to Theophrastus, waited for him to chew it. Amused at this quiet insistence, Theophrastus obediently chewed; he loved mint anyway. It was only after he had swallowed that the fellow, still wordless, led him down to the door at the end of the hall.

"Who is it, Leeks?" Theophrastus remembered the gruff voice which came through the opening door. It was "The Bull" all right.

"A scholar, Master Vadianus," said Leeks. "A brilliant scholar by his hand and brow."

"The Bull" turned and glared a moment. Then he said, "Scholar indeed, Leeks. This stripling Switzer is our 'para' Celsus."

Theophrastus was stunned to hear the name which had stung his inner ear for several nights along the road from Tübingen to Vienna. He searched Vadianus' face for some sign of gentleness or humor, but there wasn't any.

Leeks meantime was offering Vadianus an herb, too, but it wasn't a mint; he was giving Vadianus three jagged blades of the dandelion plant, and dandelion was bitter stuff. Vadianus chewed obediently; even he, Theophrastus noted, felt the silent command of the remarkable peasant. The edges of his mouth deepened, became even more severe. When he had swallowed, Leeks picked up his pouch and went out.

The silence continued; Vadianus offered no word. So Theophrastus decided to explain how his own premature nickname, which had preceded him into Vienna, came about. He spoke no more than the truth, but he seemed to take the plague and the academic indifference to it as an affront against himself. The teachers, he said, were not masters of medicine but of debate. The citizens of the town, including women and children, who were ill, the doctors were very likely to leave "to God's will"; but what if it was His will for them to bestir themselves at least enough to make the deaths around them more dignified and humane?

"As for the students," he went on, "they are not learning, and most of them are not interested in becoming healers. They will cure by the mouth, just as their teachers cure. They will take their degrees, they will put on their fine cloaks of scarlet and their glittering rings, they will kowtow to the overstuffed nobility and bilk the sick and the poor as they always have!" He had spoken freely, and now he ended breathless.

After a while Vadianus went over to a big, freshly printed text. "*Galen's Works,*" he said. "They have this copy at Tübingen, too, you know."

What a cold fish, Theophrastus thought, but he didn't say it. "Yes, sir, I know," he said.

Vadianus let the tome fall open to a random page. "Which of the humors is likely to need more bleeding?" he asked. Theophrastus shifted his feet and was silent. "You are acquainted with the humors, boy?" said "The Bull." His tone made it clear that the boy had *better* know them.

"I know them all right, sir," said Theophrastus. He could rattle them off: sanguine, phlegmatic, choleric, melancholic, but he chose not to.

"Give me an answer then," said Vadianus.

"I don't know the answer, Master Vadianus." Theophrastus was angry, but somehow impressed. He had no idea his father's friend could be so unyielding.

Vadianus turned to a second book. "Here is a more recent find, the worthy and divine Hippocrates. Father of Greek medicine. Therefore, our own." He opened the book to its flyleaf. "Recite for me his oath."

Theophrastus remembered his father praising the oath, and in truth he had intended to memorize it. But things just hadn't turned out that way.

"I–don't know it, sir."

"Innocent of Hippocrates as well?" said Vadianus, with a grim smile on his lips. He held the book up and talked as if at the binding. "You ever notice about donkeys, boy?" he said mysteriously. "There are two kinds. One kind is docile, useful, good. Give him a bit of food and water, he will work all day, he pulls his weight uphill. This kind we call a 'mule.'" He paused, set the book down and looked flush at Theophrastus, who looked as if he wanted to run somewhere.

"The other kind, he eats. He sleeps. He will not budge until it suits his fancy. And when he does move, it is not to advance. He kicks his hind legs out against a wall. This kind, this kind, 'para' Celsus von Hohenheim, we call a 'jackass.'"

"What are you saying? Are you calling me . . . ?" sputtered the boy.

"Destroying's easy, boy. Building comes hard." Vadianus had picked up the Galen tome and was advancing almost with menace toward the boy.

"You are!" shouted the boy angrily. "You're calling me . . . !"

"You green, unharnessed ass!" Vadianus now was hovering over the boy like some primeval force. "That's what

I'm calling you! That torpid brain of yours, too full of mountain cheese and wind, looks at things backward. It looks at a fir and says its line points down. But it points up too. Go looking in the world for ignorance, for evil. Oh, you'll find it. Why not go looking for the wise, the good. It's out there too. And *here*," he said, coming down hard on the Galen with the flat of his palm. "It's here in the words of these wise men. Learn from the bottom up, boy. Learn what has been learned. Learn it inside out and backward. And then—then, mind you, not before—after five years or ten applying what you know, you may stumble upon a clue toward some fresh, new way of healing!" As he concluded, he shoved the edge of the Galen tome into Theophrastus' stomach, and the boy, by a reflex movement, grabbed the edges of the book and held on.

Vadianus turned brusquely away. He walked to the narrow slit of a window and stared out, as though unconcerned. But he was hoping. Had he served his old friend Wilhelm right? Had he done what Wilhelm in a letter had urged, ". . . lash the boy's pride with words" and ". . . sting him into more book learning"? In the next minute he would know.

Although he did not turn, he listened intently to the boy's footsteps behind him. He heard them move, replacing the Galen, perhaps; then he heard them move to the door and go out. He had failed then, he thought with a sigh; so be it. But when he turned, he saw that the Galen was gone; and with it not only the new Hippocrates but the twelve-year-old translation of Plato's works by Marsilio Ficino of the Medici court. He grinned broadly; it was more than he had hoped.

Outside, no sooner had Theophrastus managed to pull

closed the door than Leeks was on him, taking two of the huge tomes from his hand.

"You're a physician, no?" said Leeks, eagerly.

"Beginning, yes."

"Ah, you physicians! You know so many wonderful secrets about man," said Leeks. His envy was so honest and so open, it was touching.

"Less than we need to know, my friend," said Theophrastus.

Leeks, who apparently found the answer pleasing, nodded quickly in appreciation and grinned. Leeks' grin was always at the ready.

"You know the virtues of the herbs?" Theophrastus asked respectfully.

"Leeks knows a few."

They had passed through the door of the building, but Leeks did not return the books to Theophrastus. He was going to carry them out to where the mare was hitched.

"Your Christian name," said Theophrastus as they walked, "surely it isn't Leeks?"

The peasant laughed merrily. "What's in a name?" he said with a shrug. "Leeks is as good as any." As they crossed the campus green, he explained that he used the leek, an herb in the onion family, as a cleanser whenever phlegm thickened along the breath passages. He made a practice of giving leeks to children with runny noses, and they had given him the nickname. He was proud of the fact that although they hated the leeks, they nevertheless flocked to his side whenever he came.

"You offered me mint," angled Theophrastus, hoping for a new clue to the herb.

"The mint is friendly. Excellent for greeting. For sweet breath."

"Which would you say is the herb that I most need?" said Theophrastus. They were standing by the mare now. Leeks cocked his head, gave Theophrastus a professional look and reopened his pouch. As Theophrastus carefully fit the three tomes in the side satchel, Leeks withdrew a long, green stalk with a rosy tint on the inside. Theophrastus had never seen it before.

He took a big, crackling bite. It was very juicy and very sour. "What is it?" he said.

"Rhubarb."

"It's what I most need?"

"For body and for mind."

"What is the principal virtue of this rhubarb?" asked Theophrastus.

"It is a purgative," said Leeks, and walked away.

Theophrastus swallowed the sour, stringy lump and shook his head. It had been a hard day.

Theophrastus quickly fell into a workable routine. Although he was formally studying astrology, geometry, and music, he used them as fillers and as chores when his energies flagged. His most interesting hours were spent with Leeks, who was eager to exchange herb lore for book learning, and with Vadianus, who had decided to give himself a course in Galen and Hippocrates as he tutored the boy—who now had a distinct blond fuzz growing on his face.

They tackled the Hippocrates first. Theophrastus found the ancient Greek to be austere but exciting company. He noted the wonderfully reasonable nature of his cures: fresh air, good diet, mild purgatives, modern bloodletting, barley broth, honey and vinegar tonics, massages and baths. And gentle as his approach was generally, forbidding his students to "cut persons," he knew also that "desperate diseases need desperate remedies." Refusing to leave his difficult cases "to the gods," he labored mightily to establish a basis of facts which would enable physicians after himself not only to diagnose ailments correctly, but to prognose, or foretell, from one set of symptoms the other signs, including death or recovery, which would follow.

And how few of these modern medical popinjays, said Theophrastus to his tutor, had the least touch of his moral stature when it came to money. When the Persian Artaxerxes offered Hippocrates a sizable fortune to help combat an epidemic which was decimating his invading army, the Greek politely but flatly turned the king down. Above all did Hippocrates' stress on the individuality of each patient impress the boy; even in epidemics, the treatment must vary with the patient. "One man's meat is another man's poison," he wrote. Theophrastus was surprised and sorry to see the last page come.

Vadianus pumped the boy ruthlessly on the facts of the text, and by way of answer he got more than he asked. He heard the facts repeated, improved, heightened in detail. And soon the boy exasperated him by answering his question with another question.

In Hippocrates' description of the woman with scarlet fever, he wanted to know why he hadn't tried an herb, or a color broth, or a modified climate? Was a barley water treatment meant as an enema or as a broth? Was another herb to be taken internally or applied externally as a poultice? And why? They would get caught up, both of them, in the reasoning and, in a kind of dispassionate rage, be at each other's throat before their senses returned.

Theophrastus was deeply grateful that Vadianus treated

him as an equal, even to these arguments; Vadianus knew that once the boy had exhausted the medical texts, there would be nothing, except perhaps Leeks and his herbs, to hold him.

For if the hours Theophrastus spent with Vadianus were interesting, those he spent with Leeks were exciting. Whenever a new herb was in full leaf or in flower or in seed, Leeks would appear at his window, and they would hike off to the wood or mountain or field to observe the herb where it lived. They would collect the herb and immediately, while the virtue was in full power, pass it around to the children who seldom failed to gather or take it into a village, to a peasant's hut or to a mother in labor.

The two of them would manage to tramp most of the day. By nightfall, the powerful, ageless man with the balding head, and the gray-eyed boy with the fuzz thickening on his chin, would be at an inn with a tankard each of red wine, the natural, unsweetened stuff, before them. Two of the tankards would go by, or three. Leeks would be telling the boy of the wonderful powers of buttercup juice for diseases of respiration; and he would wheedle from Theophrastus what Hippocrates or Galen had prescribed. Galen particularly fascinated him; not so much for the galenicals, or herb poultices which the ancient Greek made famous, but for his success story. And Theophrastus, in fact, told the story very well.

Marcus Aurelius, Emperor of Rome, mightiest citizen of the Western world, had a bellyache. He could hold no audiences, he could not hear any case with an equal mind; all the high-level business of the empire was at a standstill. It was simply no use: food—and especially cold food—did not sit well on the imperial stomach. He had called in the court physicians, or *archiatri,* to no avail. He had called in the *sagae,* or Wise Women, to no avail. Occultists, herbalists, drug peddlers, bath attendants—each was called in his turn; but the peerless stomach remained unsettled.

And then to the rescue came an unknown Greek physician from Pergamum. This outlander, returning the savage glances of the royal physicians with a contempt of his own, coolly went about his business, retaking the symptoms which they had taken a hundred times over, and made his diagnosis. The stomach was overloaded, was coated with phlegm, and would resist all foods, particularly the cold ones. He proceeded to describe for the emperor, in livid terms, all the discomforts which accrued from such an indisposition, and the emperor all too painfully recognized the accuracy of his description. "Even so, even so," murmured the emperor, over and over again. "But what, for a cure?"

Galen, whose psychology was matched only by his courtliness, answered: "For a royal stomach, apply wool saturated with spikenard."

Marcus Aurelius, no mean observer of the human predicament himself, appreciated the distinction among stomachs but nevertheless demanded, "And what, for *any* stomach?"

Galen, after he had bowed, spoke firmly: "A flagon of hot wine spiced heavily with red pepper."

Marcus Aurelius dismissed his audience. After a brief meditation on stomachs, he chose the hot wine and pepper. Within two hours the emperor began to recover; top-secret and high-level affairs continued as usual, and the whole of the civilized world, so to speak, breathed a little easier.

"That red pepper," laughed Leeks into his tankard.

"Agh!" And once, he sobered suddenly and added, "How comforting to know that even kings have stomachs!"

What was important to them both was the even exchange, the book knowledge of Theophrastus for the practical knowledge of Leeks. Noting that the boy shared a love for wine, he gave him a piece of practical advice: "Cabbage is the secret, boy. Before wine, cabbage; after— the morning after—sauerkraut juice."

And Theophrastus, remembering some Latin he had translated for Erhard in Villach, read to him a passage from the Roman, Cato: "If you wish to drink much at a banquet, before dinner dip cabbage in vinegar and eat as much as you will. When you have dined, eat five leaves. The cabbage will make you as fit as if you had had nothing and you can drink as much as you will." At this bit of wisdom, they clinked tankards and drank on.

He had began to piece together Leeks' story, mostly from the older children who tagged along, when this friendship, too, ended abruptly and tragically. No one seemed to remember his real name; but he had been a farmer with a fairly large family somewhere across the mountains to the west. One by one, beginning with his wife, his family died of chills and fevers, of distempers and diseases which many doctors treated but none cured. When his last child, a daughter of five, died of a fever, he buried her under a cypress and never turned another furrow.

The deaths, some said, touched his mind, for quietly he began to preach a dangerous philosophy which he dispensed freely with his herbs. He believed that property belonged to everybody—or rather that it belonged neither to the Church nor to the lords but to God. He began to help himself to his basic needs; never did he take more than he needed, but he always had his own fill, and cheerfully doled out enough for those around him. Everyone knew of his belief, even the Church and feudal officials, but such was the selflessness of the man that they agreed to overlook it.

It was Leeks' practice to disappear without notice, to join the Brothers of the Common Lot, one of the sects devoted to spiritual ends, for a week or two, before he rejoined his Vienna haunts. But this time he had disappeared for more than a month, and Theophrastus went to Vadianus for news.

"Have you seen Leeks lately?"

Vadianus, who had been so gloomy for a week that his classes had suffered, answered curtly. "You want to see him now? He's hanging in the square." His voice quivered with rage.

Thunderstruck, the boy groped for the stool nearby to catch his weight.

"He's dead," said Vadianus, his fist pounding the mantel. "They've executed him for a heretic, the fools!"

Friday, the week before, on the night of a great storm, the homeless Leeks had found the sacristy door of the cathedral unlocked. Inside, there was a cask of altar wine, the sweetened stuff from Medoc, which he drank from the Mass chalice. He had spread a sacred tapestry on the stone floor and, no doubt to those who knew him, held a private little ritual to the Great Mother through whose grace came the fruits of the earth. The next morning the sexton found him lying there in a blissful stupor.

Bishop Beratz of Vienna, an ecclesiast very active in the Inquisition, pronounced it diabolism and sacrilege. Imprisoned for two days, Leeks was tried in secret on the third; on the fourth he was pronounced guilty of conducting a black Mass in the presence of demons; on the fifth, he was given "The Question," a trial by torture whereby he was "purified" of the sacred wine and persuaded to tell the truth by stringing him upside down and flushing his body through the anus until water poured freely through the mouth. On the sixth day at high noon, with clusters of his children looking on, he was hanged from the public gallows.

"He . . . he was your friend. Your friend!" said Theophrastus, rising. "You could have saved him!"

"The Inquisition, boy . . . !" growled Vadianus, his voice trailing away. "You don't know what you say."

"The body. It is still hanging in the square?" Theophrastus could at least bury his friend with dignity.

Vadianus shrugged. "The body was approved for the dissection."

So it was Leeks' body the medical students would watch being dismembered! The thought of this final desecration galvanized the boy into action. He ran across campus, to the little stage where the *Commedia* players often performed their ribald productions. If the body was not yet on the stage, there was some chance, somehow, of saving him from at least this. But a crowd—students and citizens, children and animals—had already gathered, and a local barber called Fat Fritz was wheeling in the body in a wooden wheelbarrow.

To make a scene now, Theophrastus saw, would only add to the dishonor; and perhaps, even in death, Leeks through his dissected body would be serving a purpose. The boy stood numbly by and watched the proceedings.

Presiding over the scene below was a black-robed professor who sat perched in an elevated little stand. He was removed from the gore and the odors of the dissection, as befit his dignity and station. From a big illustrated text in his hand he would call out the part as, below, Fat Fritz would cut it out, skewer it on the tip of his blade and hold it out under the noses of the crowd for inspection.

Fat Fritz, it turned out, loved dissections. Long forbidden by the Church, they had recently been permitted on prisoners who had been condemned to hell-fire anyway; and Fritz, who wielded his tools with a flourish, boasted of having "analyzed" 112 heads. For Fat Fritz was by no means a mere barber, he was an inveterate showman. He made his dissections live. His appearance was striking: from the red beard and freckles to the stiff, rusty hairs growing between the powerful knuckles; the way he ran his loaded wheelbarrow up the little ramp and unceremoniously dumped it; the extravagant air with which he extracted each of his tools—the cleaver, the pairs of scalpels, plain and hooked; the needle-like probe and the poker for keeping the edges honed—all was designed to catch and keep a crowd.

The professor overhead was already restive. This, quite obviously, was not a part of his job which he relished. "We will begin," he announced.

Fritz drew a hooked scalpel on a straight line from the sternum to the pelvis. The pressure was uneven; at the abdomen several loops of intestine oozed through. The crowd, especially the children who no longer associated the corpse with Leeks, gasped and pressed forward.

The dissection proved a fiasco in every way. But it was not merely the tone. The naming of the parts itself was absurd. The professor, who went with absolute strictness by the book, called out parts which did not exist in the human anatomy; and Fat Fritz, always with a wry superiority which came with his 112 dissections, dug up parts not mentioned in the professor's text. And when the professor, going by the book, insisted on calling the pipe attached to the lungs the "foodpipe," Theophrastus, feeling an overpowering disgust, left the stage.

For a week he stayed in his room, not even going out to eat. Continuing his studies at the University of Vienna was out of the question, for indeed, he had other problems. A huge nameless vision, one which had begun years ago with the burning of Crazy Mary and the death of his mother, which had grown with the miner's disease at Villach and the plague at Tübingen, came sharply into focus. Whatever the beauty of mountains and woods, whatever the incidental kindness and happiness of children, he saw the world of men as a world of pain.

He was spared the task of telling Vadianus of his plan to move on, for in another week, the University of Vienna was closed with the plague.

7

EVEN THE CONSUMING DESIRE to learn how to heal left him now. In this new world which he had entered, so full of cruelty and vengeance and pain, young Hohenheim could find no inner peace, no certainty of any kind. The refrain, "Who can heal the mind?" which his father had so casually uttered so long ago, recurred in his mind as if to mock him.

Not that he hadn't found exciting clues. There was the crotchety grandfather, one hundred years old, who, after extreme unction by the local priest, had shaken off the cleric with the words, "Get that foolishness out of here. I'm going to live to smell another spring."

There were the miraculous cures—the kidney touched by the Great Mother, the paralyzed limb made whole when St. Catherine breathed upon it in a dream, the ulcers which shriveled away when the Angel Gabriel touched the waters of the spa. In fact, the young man had noted clearly the tiny symptoms—the look of the eye, the twitch

of the mouth, the random movements of the hand—which
foretold madness; and had noted, too, similar but quite
different signs which indicated not derangement but a
surpassing health of the mind.

But now the anguish of his own mind eclipsed his
concern for the minds of others. Again and again he cast
about, trying to find the source of this anguish. The
violence of the world around him moved him. But the
deepest source of his problems, he decided, was that it
seemed to him that among men there *must* be a few who
had a true knowledge, who knew not only the casual
system of facts—the rules of grammar and logic, the
description of stones and stars, the names and number of
the parts of the dismembered body—but the profound, the
mystic meanings behind these things. They must know
how the forms of grammar embodied the growth of a
thought, what a stone or a star really was, in its totality,
in and of itself. They must know how a man, turning all
his mental and psychic powers upon his own body, in self-
knowledge, could see what the greatest of men had seen—
a world too small to matter in a world too vast to imagine.

To become a doctor suddenly seemed to him too trivial;
what seemed absolutely essential was to become a man.
And to him, the only being with this universal thirst, who
directed himself to the higher power, whatever it was,
could be man. But most were blind, or foolish, or
craven.

Indeed, the vast number of beings which he had met to
date, moving around on two legs more or less upright,
seemed animal. He thought of his own father, Wilhelm,
gratefully, but sensed absolutely that his own thirst was
overwhelmingly bigger than his father's. Even stern, dear
Vadianus seemed, for all his forthrightness, caught up in a

quest for social position and an intellectual game. As for the rest, the piddling ideals and money-minded practice of the doctors disgusted him, and the very subjects which excited his professors seemed to him accepted forms of madness.

If Truth existed, no matter how unpopular, it must be known. If God, in order to teach a respect for His Law, had visited men with diseases, the lesson of them must be learned. If He, in His mercy, had hidden the cures to these diseases in the virtues of plants and in minerals and in animals, in the earths, the waters, the air and the stars, it surely must be the abiding passion of a physician, one who had first and foremost become a man, to discover those cures. Young Hohenheim was painfully aware that he knew very little; but where was the man who knew more, more truly worth knowing, not the two-faced knowledge of books but the humble and all-powerful facts of life? No man he had met had matched his own thirst to know; no man seemed even to care.

About a month before Leeks' death, a certain man set afire the intellects of Europe. Johannes Heidenberg of Tritheim until then was a highly respected abbot of Sponheim. His reputation had long since been established both locally and nationally as a teacher of ethics—not abstractly from books, but in the practical everyday problems—and as that kind of connoisseur of art and poetry in whose presence artists and art flourish and grow. Students flocked to him from all parts of Germany.

But Trithemius, not content with these fragments, aimed for the kind of knowledge which was power, but power of a very real, practical sort, which can transform bodies, reform minds and discover the soul itself. He was attracted to the Cabala, the secret key to the occult sciences, and was soon absorbed in it. With amazing swiftness, he translated the message of the book into facts, into actions; the enigmatic sayings and signs seemed to him perfectly clear. He fast acquired the power, according to his students and even to some of his severest critics, of reading the thoughts of others and of transmitting to others thoughts of his own. He had the power of putting others into a trance which healed their disorders.

At last, after seven years of cabalistic disciplines and practice, he announced, without fanfare, that he could teach his students how to put themselves into such states so that they learned more about themselves. "Man, know thyself," the motto of Socrates, he adopted for his own, and stated that, helpful though Church ritual and sacrament were, they did not lead so directly or so inevitably to self-knowledge.

Inevitably, his inoffensive reputation as a master of ethics and of art took on suspicious overtones. For now, although he himself never claimed the titles, he became known as a magus, as an adept in "white" magic. The Church, which for good or evil had an eye on and a finger in everything these days, nervously overlooked Trithemius. Nothing but the constructive and the good seemed to come from him and his students. But when he publicly defended the victims of the Holy Inquisition, and denied that witches existed "out of nature," it moved in. The Church summarily removed the abbot from his abbey in Sponheim.

Vadianus, in one of his last classes with young Hohenheim, was outraged by the Church's highhandedness. "A man should have his say before he's fired," he said hotly.

Theophrastus, then not yet overwhelmed by his world of pain, remembered the long hours required to wrest even a single fact about a mineral through chemistry. Knowledge, he felt at the time, came painfully, slowly, and not in a divine deluge such as Trithemius seemed to describe. Little sympathy as he had for the Church, he had less for the Abbot of Sponheim.

"He got what he deserves," said the youth.

Vadianus, about to continue his denunciation, stopped short. "The longer I know you, the more you are a puzzle!" he said testily. "Here is Trithemius, a rebel like yourself, a man whose mind cries out for working room. Here are these others, who set his mind in chains. And whose side are you on? You side with the forgers of the chains!"

"He's an impostor."

"How do you know?"

"He heaps his knowledge by the haystack. I glean it straw by straw. That's how I know."

Vadianus was delighted. He never showed it, but the hardheaded approach, the abruptness with which young Hohenheim gave his views seemed to come from an utter fearlessness, and this fearlessness added to his own courage. His answers were so honest and direct that they failed somehow to offend. The needle was in and out before the mind took note of the puncture.

"But," said Vadianus, slowly forming the thought, "what if he has found a quicker way to know? What if he's opened some new faculty of the human mind?"

"Knowledge is experiment," scoffed Hohenheim. "Experiment, pure and simple."

"Experiment with *aquas,* alkalis, with metals, with salts?

What if Trithemius experiments with himself—his body, his mind, his soul?"

And for the first time in six months, the youth was stumped. His eyes glared; he was furious. But he had no answer. He started to pace, angrily, as though waiting for an answer to well up within him. "That's doubletalk," he shouted at last. "That's mystical gibberish and you know it."

Vadianus was alarmed by the vehemence of Hohenheim's answer and he decided to hold his tongue.

"Have you sent thoughts?" continued the youth hotly.

"No."

"Can you put others in a trance?"

"No."

"Or heal yourself in one?"

"Perhaps a little, when I drop off to sleep," Vadianus said in a tone carefully casual. "But you know as well as I. That a million men are innocent of these powers, is no proof that the powers don't exist. I've read three dozen books; no serf in Christendom has read a word."

"You and your precious logic," cried Hohenheim, as though wounded. "Logic is a puny little poodle madly chasing its own tail. Not logical, but analogical for me. Analogy and sense. To know is not to think, thinking's too easy. To see, to hear, to feel—this is to know . . . !" He said this as if he had just formulated something which had been a long while aborning inside. He stopped short and picked up his Ficino *Plato*. Then, walking over to the door he said, very quietly:

"Trithemius is a self-deluded devil, or . . ."

"Or what?"

"Or he's the teacher I've been waiting for," said Hohenheim and walked out.

Vadianus stared at the closed door. A twinge of pain stabbed at his chest. He, Vadianus, was not that teacher. Hohenheim had not meant to offend, and that made the offense all the greater. He took a deep breath: he had not realized that the boy meant so much to him. Well, he had sharpened the boy's mind. He had encouraged a critical, hardheaded outlook as companion to an eager open-mindedness in his charge. His friend's son would instinctively refuse to take any thing, any idea or any person at face value. Yes, if he had not been *the* teacher in this fiery young man's life, he was certainly one of his teachers. And that was enough.

Ferrara University in Italy had for some time attracted Hohenheim. It was Platonist rather than Aristotelian, and from the Ficino book he knew that his mind, the very fabric of it, was Platonist. But school, any school, promised only more of the dreariness which had already disheartened him.

At Ferrara, news of Trithemius and of his powers continued to come to him. In his studies with Dr. Niccolo Leoniceno on the terrifying new "love pestilence" or "French disease" which was ravaging Europe, he heard the aged doctor refer again and again to Trithemius' explanation of the cause. When war broke out between the French King Francis and the German Emperor Maximilian, and Hohenheim was mustered into service as a surgeon, he met soldiers and pilgrims and clergymen who spoke of him.

And so at length, when he was free again to travel, it was to Trithemius, who now resided in Würzburg, Germany, that he turned. He had made no conscious choice; the decision seemed somehow to have made itself. He would beard the lion in his den; he would decide once and for all whether, or rather how, the charlatan could be mistaken for a sage.

It was a mild evening in May, 1515, when young Hohenheim opened the door of the guild hall where Trithemius was holding his meetings. Some daylight still filtered in through the windows, but candles, perhaps ceremonial, were lit inside. A group of men of all ages sat in a rough semicircle on wooden benches. Addressing them stood a single figure dressed in a long white cassock with its cowl thrown back, the silver hair belying the striking young face. No sooner had the door opened than the speaker stopped his lecture and spoke to Hohenheim.

"So there you are at last! Come in, come in!" he said, almost beside himself with joy.

Hohenheim was outraged at the cheap trick. "I've never been here before," he sputtered, all the more angry that he had lost his composure.

"Come to the fore, my son. Sit here." The speaker motioned to an empty place on a bench in the front row. So cheerful was the voice, so perfectly convinced that Hohenheim would comply that there was no question of refusing. Reluctantly, and indignantly, Theophrastus walked through the listeners to the vacant spot.

"I am Johannes, called Trithemius. The place is yours. Please sit."

Young Hohenheim had recovered some of his composure. "Thank you," he said, a thin veil of courtesy over his anger. "But I prefer to stand."

"Of course!" said Trithemius, grinning rapturously. "My manners fail me! It's time to stand," he said to the crowd. "Let us all stand and meet this young man here."

The audience stood.

"Fathers and brothers," said Trithemius happily, "meet here Philippus Theophrastus Bombastus von Hohenheim." He lingered playfully on the long name.

There was a murmur of greetings and a random clasping of arms. But Theophrastus was only vaguely aware of it. He was stunned. Not only did Trithemius know his full name, but someone had told him that he was coming. But he hadn't told a soul. Who, then? He sat down, and as he did so, the others followed suit. In a moment, deftly and gently, Trithemius had resumed his talk.

Young Hohenheim was a turmoil of feeling. He was by turns embarrassed, resentful, abashed. After the feelings subsided a bit, he noticed that not only Trithemius him- self but all those who listened, despite his angry, almost violent entrance, had forgotten about him. Gratefully, he settled into the seat and began to listen.

In a voice wonderfully serene, the gray-haired figure was describing two kinds of knowledge. The one, he said, was a knowledge of nature. Nature spoke not in words but in things, and this knowledge, compiled and ordered in books, was both praiseworthy and useful. It demanded painstak- ing care, and those dedicated to its discovery must believe as little as could be proved. But such knowledge, the piecemeal analysis and synthesis of nature, was endless and it inevitably proved futile to the individual man.

Each individual owed it to himself to pursue a second and higher kind of knowledge: the knowledge of self. For however complete and accurate and helpful the knowledge of nature may become, it advances the individual not a whit in the great work which is himself. He must at long last come to grips with his own mind. The mind has powers which lie asleep until they are roused; but once roused and exercised, these powers bring a knowledge which is no longer fragmentary and piecemeal.

The mind, integrated and balanced, using its full powers harmoniously, sees the whole. And this new knowledge is different from both the common sense which is the mainstay and limitation of the uneducated serf and the intellect which, though it is a minor power of the human soul, is the pride and the delusion of the educated élite. Such powers as he had, said Trithemius, were by no means supernatural, but the completely natural result of tapping energies possessed but ignored by other men.

Young Hohenheim heard these words with a great happiness. His certainty that the knowledge of chemistry comes only to those who "try," could exist side by side with his Platonic urge that man, individual men with invincible will and purity of heart, was divine. He listened no more; now he was fascinated with the face before him.

Trithemius reminded the young man of a falcon, he seemed like a benign, ageless hawk. Most striking were the eyes. They were wide blue eyes, fierce by nature and softened by love, which, without being in the least abstract or vague, seemed to look *into*, rather than upon, the object of sight. The nose was hooked, at once savage and refined. And something about the mouth suggested that it had endured great pain and now, perfectly composed, was predisposed to smile at the least occasion of beauty or of humor.

Not the least striking feature of this man was the contrast of the ageless face under the shock of silver hair. But most remarkable was the overall effect—one of an extraordinary mildness. Sitting on the bench before him, young Hohenheim thought that, whether he was a genuine master of "white" magic or not, Trithemius certainly looked the part.

The master had been speaking, but Hohenheim, all eyes, had not heard a word. Now Trithemius, with a slight shift in tone, seemed to be directing his words at him. And suddenly, the young man was again listening intently.

"So as we go, each to his world, let us ask this: 'Where does all knowledge end?'" The nasal voice, rich and vibrant, was making a summary.

"In the earth's history, ours is a remarkable time. Sailors explore, discover many lands. Scholars discover manuscripts, new modes of thought. Chemists disclose the magic sealed in earths, in metals and salts. All this is to the good. But however good the exploration, however exciting the discovery, there is something better. And what is better is the man. What good to touch upon a thousand shores, to read a hundred manuscripts, to cook a mint of gold, if you are less than you can be?

"No, fathers, brothers, sons, to know, merely to know, is not enough. For we must *be*. If knowledge is of things, wisdom is of the self. Knowledge may be good; wisdom is certainly better. A 'good' which blocks a 'better' is an evil. What good, a million men, if none is wise? A million nothings, added, come to nothing. But place a one, a genuine one to the fore, and it is power. It is the one, and not the million ciphers, that has the power. Let us each, in his own world, become this one.

"So as we go, let us ask this: 'Where does all knowledge end?'"

Trithemius, unlike the professors of rhetoric in the schools, ended by asking a question. He did not "prove" an opinion. And Hohenheim, who as he listened was intently studying his knuckles, was surprised when no further words came. He looked up. The magus with a radiant smile, was talking with one of his students. The talk was over.

Whatever this Trithemius was, the young man thought, he was an extraordinary being. The least he, Hohenheim, could do was to apologize for his sullen attitude.

"It is all to the good, you know," said Trithemius as Theophrastus came near.

"What is?"

"To question until we know. To use the reason."

"You knew that I was coming. Foreknowledge is not a reasonable power."

Trithemius smiled. "Reason is one of the powers of the soul, but not the highest. And yet, it must be used. It must be exercised, fulfilled. Especially by such as you."

"Why me?"

"Why, for your work, to heal," said Trithemius, with the barest hint of a smile. "Your work to heal the mind."

So the magus knew this too, knew his most cherished thought. He could feel his last reservations, his subtlest and most inward resistance to this man, crumbling away. Let the rest of the world call Heidenberg a charlatan, mountebank, impostor: Trithemius was his teacher.

Hohenheim was surprised and pleased that Trithemius used no elaborate ritual, dark pomp, or incantatory abracadabra. Although the master possessed extrasensory powers, he chose to use them sparingly, and only in the presence of those few who would not stand agog at the phenomena. In fact, he was all business. He taught Hohenheim nothing out of books, although his book *On Witchcraft* was a best seller of the day; what he taught the young man were the staples in the training for the medita-

tive sages—some positions for the body, to relax it utterly,
and to enable it to hold a fixed position indefinitely.
Special attention was given to the spine. He taught of
some words which were "charged"—the names of virtues
or of God, to be repeated secretly and more and more
subtly, with the aim of concentrating the mind and, by
suggestion and the descent of grace, of inducing new
presences; and techniques for pinpoint listening and for
conscious, transformative breathing.

Theophrastus eagerly dedicated himself to these practices. Both gradually, and by sudden leaps, he felt himself
changing. His anger subsided. He could work for longer
periods of time without tiring. The eruptions of affection
for all living things smoothed away into a continuous glow.
He could read a paragraph and, by a keen, instant ap-
praisal of the mind which wrote it, know unerringly
whether the book was of use. He could see in minerals, in
plants, in men, by a combination of analogy and insight,
new tendencies, hidden properties, essences. And this
knowledge was dependent upon no man outside himself,
not even upon Trithemius. They seemed to have existed
within himself forever. He was prepared to stay here indefinitely.

But one morning, when Theophrastus had roused himself from the meditative trance, he felt a hand on his
shoulder.

"It's time to go, my son." Trithemius stood behind him,
smiling.

"Go where, Johannes?"

"Why, back to work, of course."

"But . . . but, the practices!" protested Hohenheim.
"They aren't mastered!"

"You need only yourself to practice," said Trithemius,

with a laugh. "Practice them as you ride. Master them as you heal, my son."

"But where, Johannes, where? Is there a place for me?"

"I know of none," said the magus, soberly. "Your place, it's everywhere. The world is wracked with illness, error, madness. Groans come from every side. Your place, Theophrastus, is to go to the next groan. Soothe it away. Transform it to a smile."

Within the hour, Theophrastus von Hohenheim, loaded with his medical satchel and a change of clothes, stood at the door. For the last time, Trithemius stood before him.

"You came as Theophrastus. But as Theophrastus you do not go."

"How, then?" said Hohenheim. "How do I go."

"As the incomparable Paracelsus." And for the first time the name, which had grated his soul, thrilled him. This precious moment he would remember over and over, not only because it rang with a new insight into himself, and who he was, but because it was the last time Paracelsus saw his teacher. Within the year, Johannes Heidenberg called Trithemius was dead.

III

PARACELSUS, THE PHYSICIAN

To be a good alchemist is to understand the chemistry of life. Medicine is not merely a science but an art. It does not consist in compounding pills and plasters and drugs of all kinds, but it deals with the processes of life which must be understood before they can be guided. A powerful will may cure when doubt would end in failure. The character of the physician may act more powerfully upon the patient than all the drugs employed.

PARACELSUS

8

WHEN PARACELSUS LEFT his master teacher, he
made a trip "around the world." He went not only
to the next groan but to the next cure. Traditional medicine
had proved itself powerless, and he scorned it; but he
scorned no cure, however vile, that worked, and no person,
however humble, who could heal so much as a wart. He
consulted necromancers and folk doctors; he questioned
witches and the most outlandish quack. He listened respectfully to any man or woman who had a reputation for
healing any sort of disorder. For this, of course, the
orthodox doctors and their medical associations, or guilds,
could not bring themselves to forgive him. And to add
injury to insult, news began to trickle in of this outrageous Paracelsus and his cures—cures not only of money-
less peasants whom these men had abandoned but also of
noblemen whom they had pronounced incurable.

By horse, by boat, by foot, he traveled on, observing,
experimenting, treating, the energy sparkling in the gray

eyes, the familiar satchel all the while filling out with new arcana, secret new medicines. His every move seemed calculated to offend the settled and the smug. In England, he ignored Oxford and Cambridge to work with miners in Cornwall. In Russia, he sided with the Tartars invading Moscow and, thundering over the tundra with the invaders, left with them a potent lice powder to ease the chafe of the saddles. Many a battle line he watched from a hill, saw it waver and dissolve, watched it advance and retreat and then, as the wounded piled up—in the Netherlands, in Romagna, in Naples, Denmark, France—he moved in with a shudder and a sigh to mend the grisliest of wounds, under the colors of both sides.

In Constantinople he acquired from another magus the powerful drug, laudanum, new to Europe, which could relieve the pain of the most severe of wounds. In Palestine, in Arabia, and in Egypt he learned from magi and adepts and yogis, new techniques for calming and empowering the mind, new insights into the bewitched and the epileptic, the hysterical, and the insane.

One midnight would find him dozing among the corpses on a field of battle; the end of the next day would find him rousting boisterously with a teamster whom he had just treated; a third evening would find him bedded down in the most sumptuous guest room of a duchy. He treated peasantry and nobility with perfect indifference, and only the truly great or the hopelessly sick among the powerful could bring themselves to stomach him.

Meanwhile, his reputation among the lowly was fast becoming legend, while his name among the gentry was becoming an enigma compounded of a curse and a hope. In Copenhagen, he successfully treated the aging Queen Mother of King Christian; in the Duchy of Baden, he cured the Margrave Philip of a chronic diarrhea (and was bilked of his fee). By the time he returned to Germany to settle down, the patients whom he had returned to health included eighteen princes. Everywhere he went he showed a pointed disregard for power and a passionate regard for man. And he seldom overlooked clues to two resources for healing: the new chemistry which, although the vocabulary of science did not yet exist, was advancing by leaps and bounds; and any symptom or insight into the workings of the mind.

It was on this trip that Paracelsus acquired the sword which never left his side, even in sleep, until his death. The sword, he said, had been given him by a hangman who had given up his trade: the sword of death became the sword of truth. The weapon had one extraordinary feature—its pommel was hollow. And Paracelsus never lost a chance to state that in the pommel was the most potent and most miraculous medicine in the world.

He had spent the last year of his odyssey working in the mercury mines on the Dalmatian coast. When he moved on, he unexpectedly found himself near Villach, and the image of his father came powerfully into his mind. Years before, Wilhelm had written a postscript which stated: "Come home a doctor. Not before." The words, stern and thrilling, had inspired him. He knew that the word "doctor" was not a question of a mere diploma; Wilhelm quietly, as did Paracelsus openly, scorned them. And now, despite the fame he was fast acquiring, Paracelsus a bit nervously surveyed his career. Was he a doctor in his father's eyes? In hundreds of cases he had had the wisdom not to hinder the healing process, and he had helped in a few. Yes, he might safely return.

As luck would have it, he rode into Villach as Wilhelm

was riding out. Their glances met; they simply stopped
their mounts and looked at each other. Each was older,
yet somehow more himself. Wilhelm was a bit relieved. He
had heard many rumors about his son, most of them bad,
but after a deep look he nodded and smiled. He liked
what he saw.

Wilhelm spoke first, using his son's new name with a
gentle mockery. "Will 'Paracelsus' mend a broken arm?"
he said. And again the two of them, as they had some
fifteen years before, rode out together to attend a patient.
The left forearm of a cowherd had been fractured by the
kick of a bull. With the bleeding season upon them, the
two barber-surgeons of the area, whose job it was to mend
fractured bones, were too busy to take on any new cases,
and the cowherd was left to an even busier Wilhelm.

Old Wilhelm stayed in the background, letting his son
mend the bone. He watched casually, yet intently, as
Paracelsus, using a board for traction, found the two
jagged ends, reset them and fixed them into place with
bandages and splints. But these matters of technique were
secondary; what impressed Wilhelm was something else.
They were returning to the town when for no apparent
reason he said, "You mind his pain as if it were your own,
boy. I am proud." And somewhere deep inside, Paracelsus
felt that he had passed his most difficult test. He was a
doctor at last.

In a week he moved on. Each of the Hohenheims had
his own world; both knew and rejoiced over the fact. But
Paracelsus took with him a desire to settle down, to enjoy the peace his aging father had.

Strasbourg was a promising town. The printing press
there, one of the best in Germany, could print the pam-
phlets, monographs and books which he had begun to

write. At nearby Schlettstadt was the school of Leeks'
friends, the Brethren of the Common Lot. And above all,
Strasbourg featured the only school in all of Germany
in which surgeons were regarded as the equals of the
"doctors of physic" or physicians. And so to Strasbourg
Paracelsus came.

He was of course aware that his reputation, quite correctly, made him an enemy of all traditional schools. But
the School of Surgery at Strasbourg seemed to be shaking
off the traditional. Besides the new status given to surgeons, the staff included some of the most celebrated doctors of their day, men who seemed to Paracelsus to be
stepping boldly off in a promising direction. One of the
two heads of the School of Surgery, Hieronymus Brunswick, had written the first chemical textbook in Europe;
Dr. Vendelinus Hock, an expert at public dissections, not
only wielded the scalpel himself but lectured not in the
traditional Latin but in vernacular German; and the other
head of the school, Dr. Hans von Gerstoff, had the reputation as of being the fastest knife in Germany. In times
when amputations were performed with nothing stronger
than whiskey to deaden the pain, the only humane oper-
ation was the fast one. Besides, the new School of Surgery
had proudly advertised that it was seeking new techniques
as well as the best teachers.

Paracelsus felt sure that he would qualify for one of the
new posts. He moved into the city. He paid his citizenship
tax to the city fathers. He also paid his membership fee to
the local union, becoming a bonafide member of the Guild
of the Alfalfa, an organization which lumped with doctors,
tradesmen such as millers, grain merchants and manu-
facturers of starch. The school had a rudimentary laboratory, but his own experience was far beyond anything in

Dr. Brunswick's text, so he located living quarters with a basement to house his own chemicals, quiet enough to permit him to write his books.

Before coming to town, he had written a letter of introduction informing the school of his hope to join the staff. The letter had not been answered, but with so much unrest throughout the German countryside, the lack did not trouble him. When he arrived he sent a second note; but this too failed to stir up an answer. He had been rejected then, he thought; but perhaps, if he appeared in person he might dispel the negative aspects of his reputation.

He went to the school and asked a servant to take in to Dr. Brunswick a rolled sign, a kind of sheepskin shingle, which read:

Paracelsus von Hohenheim

Doctor of Both Medicines

Physic & Surgery

A half hour passed before the servant, looking vaguely insolent, returned from the room and announced: "Dr. Brunswick has a moment now."

Paracelsus was surprised to find that Dr. Brunswick was not alone. Vendelinus Hock and Hans von Gerstoff were with him. And neither of these rose to go as he entered; he would be answering to the three together. He knew in the instant that all three knew that he had applied, and that the conversation which preceded his arrival was about him. Dr. Brunswick rose from his chair with a perfunctory smile. He did not extend his arm in greeting. A long, awkward moment passed as no one spoke.

"You understand, von Hohenheim," stammered **Dr.** Brunswick at last, "the school must be selective."

"I understand," said Paracelsus cheerfully.

"It's a question of need," said Dr. von Gerstoff quickly. "Our staff must fill our very special needs. . . ."

"Of course," said Paracelsus affably. "Which special needs?"

Vendelinus Hock was a picture of spite. "There is no room for charlatans at this school," he said. His mouth, like a lizard's, had no lips; the yellowish texture of his pock-marked face made his fierce, coal-black eyes stand out all the more.

"I should hope not," said Paracelsus mildly. "I should hope we have no charlatans in this room."

Dr. Brunswick, aware that Paracelsus had correctly sensed their opposition to him, relented. "The salts of metals that you use. They're poisons!" he blurted out.

"Of course they're poisons, my good doctor," cried Paracelsus, grateful for the chance to talk shop. "Everything is poison in excess. It's dosage, dosage. The secret is in the dosage!" In another minute he was talking about the salts of mercury and about the amalgams being alloyed in the Dalmatian mines. Mercury, he said, was indicated for the new French disease, and it was just a question of finding the correct means of injecting it into the body. But the conversation had quickly become too friendly, and Dr. von Gerstoff cut him off.

"But how can you call yourself a surgeon?" he said in a flat voice. His eyes had flown open, as wide as an owl's. "You have opposed our practice in every detail!"

The interruption gave Paracelsus pause. He looked squarely at Hans von Gerstoff, into his wide, slightly vacant eyes. He respected the doctor's reputation as an expert craftsman with the knife; it lessened agony. And looking at him, Paracelsus pictured him as the first army surgeon he had ever seen.

A dozen years back, he had walked out of a classroom in Ferrara, Italy, onto a field of battle, and as he moved in a daze from soldier to soldier, trying to make one here, one there as comfortable as possible, he came across a ghastly figure.

From his stocking cap to his wooden brogues—his bare, hairy arms, his long leather apron, his buskins cross-strapped over his shins—this figure was covered with blood. There was not an unsmudged inch upon him anywhere; even the big brandy pouch across his back, from which he occasionally paused to take a nip, was splattered with fresh blood. He was sitting on a fallen saddle, next to a fire, stropping a long, hooked scalpel on an iron poker which hung from his belt. Around him in various attitudes of agony lay a dozen soldiers, with more gathering by the minute.

One soldier near the surgeon had brought up a comrade with a shattered arm; a dozen yards away another soldier, an arrow in horrid comedy sticking out of his buttock, was hobbling onto the scene; next to him, half running and half crawling came a third trying with his arms to keep his own intestines from trickling to the earth. The scene was a common war scene, thought Paracelsus; Dr. von Gerstoff had no doubt had his training like all barber-surgeons of the day, on the field of battle. But would he have handled the mangled arm as virtually all surgeons did? For that surgeon just outside Ferrara, once he felt the gold piece in his palm, was fast with the blade, too.

Motioning the comrade to sit on the legs of the wounded soldier, he himself had put a knee on his chest; had given him a quick swallow of brandy; and in a trice had cut off the arm at the elbow. There was very little time for the blood to spurt, though spurt it did, for in the next instant the surgeon had lifted a branding iron from the glowing coals nearby and had applied it to the stump. The soldier, who had borne the wound noiselessly and the amputation with only a groan, screamed at the smoldering brand and passed out. He did not feel the surgeon swab the stump with boiling pitch; he would be lucky, if he recovered from the shock, to feel anything more at all.

"It is true, doctor," said Paracelsus quietly. "We kill more than we cure."

"Our best is not enough, I've said as much," retorted Dr. von Gerstoff. "But how can we improve?"

"By striking out afresh. By trusting less to books and more to the fire, the brain, the eye!" Speaking with suppressed excitement, Paracelsus described the surgical procedure of the day, stage by stage, and suggested his own improvements. Brandy—alcohol of any kind—did not deaden the pain enough and increased the bleeding besides. There are drugs, he said, referring darkly to his secret laudanum, which are far more effective; they are an intrusion upon the body, but considering the shock of amputation, a necessary and lesser evil. The branding of amputated stumps was barbarous; there are effective styptics for smaller wounds, and new ways, perhaps tying the blood vessels, should be attempted.

As for the oils, salves, the unguents and the boiling pitch whose function it was to bring forth the "laudable pus," which was a sign of healing, the whole theory was absurd. "Keep the wound clean and it will heal itself," he said. "The bad surgeon insists that he heals, the good surgeon knows that he only nurses. Overmedication by doctors of physic, unnecessary cutting by doctors of surgery are far too common. And the common practice of bleeding, so close to the purses of the surgeon, is futile."

Paracelsus stopped short; if he permitted himself another sentence, he knew, he would be denouncing some practice which one of his colleagues held dear, and it was not his intention to offend. The practice of bleeding was especially touchy just now, since Dr. von Gerstoff had been recently involved, indirectly, in a malpractice suit arising from what at first had seemed a routine case of bloodletting.

But Dr. Brunswick was not content to let the subject go. "I've noticed it, I've noticed as much myself," he said vehemently. He was obviously repeating an opinion which he had already emphasized to his two compeers. "The fever subsides because the blood is gone. But when the blood returns, the fever returns."

Dr. Hock, meantime, was smoldering. He had sat a little back, out of the circle, watching developments, sure that the impostor would sooner or later snare himself in his own words. But the conversation continued to take bad turns. He couldn't believe his ears. The impostor had charmed one of his colleagues into silence and had actually won the other over. And worst of all, they were actually about to discuss the Oberdorf case openly with this upstart Paracelsus.

"Have you lost your wits?" he hissed. "This man, a surgeon? He knows nothing of anatomy!"

"He knows a little," said Paracelsus wryly.

"How can you?" said Dr. Hock, turning on him. "You openly oppose dissections. You call them 'side shows'!"

"If you conduct them so, they *are* side shows. Besides, dissections are greatly overrated."

"Perhaps you will conduct my next dissection," Dr. Hock said hotly.

Paracelsus paused. At least Vendelinus Hock was no hypocrite. He hated Paracelsus and did not try to hide it.

"You teach the body dead, Dr. Hock," he said at length. "I teach it live. Tell me, sir: how many ill bodies have you brought back to health?"

"I am a specialist in dissections, sir. It is not my job to heal."

"Dr. Hock, I will accept your challenge if you accept mine. I will conduct your next dissection if you will diagnose my next patient." Vendelinus did not deign to answer and Paracelsus went on. "Dissection. It's a beginning, doctor, but no more. Out of a bloody pulp you snip a stomach. But what is this piece of dying meat to me? What is it to the thief it came from? No doubt you say a stomach is a stomach: it looks and acts the same as others. Well, yes and no. There are a hundred kinds of stomach. One digests little, one much; one receives cabbage like ambrosia, one like the plague. Surely you will agree that the Paracelsus stomach is altogether different from the Hock?" Dr. Brunswick laughed aloud; Hock was an insufferable prig. And a merry glint entered the staring eyes of Hans von Gerstoff.

But Dr. Hock was on his feet before von Gerstoff, fuming. "To the man who calls you 'fool,' you smile," he said, and wheeled away toward a window. He stood there looking out, in a near state of apoplexy: again and again he had warned Brunswick and von Gerstoff to avoid the Oberdorf case at all costs, and he himself had brought it out into the open.

What he had said was true: Paracelsus had not bothered to hide his opinion that the case was the work of thieves and fools.

Petrus Oberdorf, a councilman of the powerful Weavers Guild, was of a sanguine humor and, therefore, as all good Galenist doctors knew, wanted a lot of bleeding. Also like sanguine men, Petrus was, within a certain limit, of a cheerful disposition. But once this limit was exceeded, something—perhaps the humor—turned him into an implacable and lifelong foe. Now, bloodletting was beneath Dr. von Gerstoff as a rule; but Mrs. von Gerstoff had a keen eye for the inwrought brocades imported from the Orient, and Petrus, a man of many and recurring ills, agreed to barter an occasional bolt of the stuff for the personal attention of the doctor. It was a gentleman's agreement which had worked smoothly for a dozen years.

It worked until a nick from the doctor's scalpel became infected. The irritation around the nick—on the inside of the left ankle—became a feverish clot; the clot became an ulcer; and ulcers, unfortunately, were not the specialty of Hans von Gerstoff. Ulcers were the specialty of one Dr. Stanislaus Schimmler who lived in the most resplendent house in his section of Strasbourg, across town.

Dr. Schimmler, everyone knew, was excellent but expensive. He conducted his house calls with a certain flair, even to spraying select sick rooms with a purifying cologne. His price was high. At the Oberdorf house Dr. Schimmler, after thumbing up the fluids of the ulcer and contemplating it in a profound hush, prescribed *tinctura arabialis,* an exotic oil available only at the Heinemann apothecary, which would soften the clot and sublime away the swelling.

Unfortunately, the clot only spread and the swelling,

mottled now with pus, became uglier than ever. So the elegant doctor prescribed a *mumia*, a bit more expensive being the ground powder of an Egyptian mummy but far more effective. But the moon turned out to be wrong for the *mumia*, and the angry swelling by now required another bleeding by Hans von Gerstoff.

One look at the ankle infuriated Dr. von Gerstoff; he wanted no part of a failure. But he complied. It came to a question of professional ethics. But when this second nick also ulcerated, and later, a third, he balked. He withdrew from the case, in spite of the fact that Mrs. von Gerstoff needed another bolt of the latest design to finish her most striking farthingale to date.

What was already a mess turned quickly into a scandal. A series of fourteen medications had been prescribed by Dr. Schimmler, all of them available only at the Heinemann apothecary; and this all-out patient care had succeeded only in turning the toes gray, in puffing the entire left foot into a greenish-brown tuber and in making the slightest movement, even, according to Petrus Oberdorf, of his eyelids, an intolerable pain. So now the patient with the poison in his leg permitted some of the poisonous vapors to discolor his brain: he plotted revenge.

Petrus still thought of Hans von Gerstoff as his friend, despite random doubts; but against Stanislaus Schimmler he filed a malpractice suit. Not that he expected to win; he knew despite the vapors that malpractice, without a doctor on his side, was nigh impossible to prove. But he had other plans. Petrus was born a businessman, and he knew his sums: he added the Schimmler house with the Heinemann glitter and came up with fraud. He had saved not only the prescriptions but samples of all the rare medications. He knew only too well what he had paid out the past four months, and, using a reputable apothecary, he discovered what the medications were actually worth. The sum came to twenty-three guilders; he had paid out 2507 guilders! Arnold Heinemann steadfastly refused to name Dr. Schimmler, but he did state categorically that his cut of "whatever the profits" came only to twenty-five guilders on the hundred.

The case never came to court. Dr. von Gerstoff was obliged to amputate, and the once cheerful Petrus, in spite of a perfect performance by his friend Hans, died of bleeding within a week. Medical circles buzzed with the news and Paracelsus, as usual, spoke his mind.

Paracelsus avoided mentioning the case by name, but he did state that such infections, even some which looked fairly ghastly, could be cleared away internally, by restoring the alchemical balance in the blood. He spoke warmly, citing cases and outlining new possibilities, when he noticed that no one, not even Dr. Brunswick, was disposed to agree. He stopped abruptly.

"Infections healed internally?" said Dr. Brunswick. "How?"

"By enriching the blood with special medications, special drugs and foods. Sometimes by fasting."

"But it's absurd, the whole idea," said Dr. von Gerstoff. "Sheer nonsense!"

"New flesh in wounds forms from within. Why is it nonsense?"

"But nowhere," sputtered Dr. Brunswick, almost aghast at the idea, "nowhere in any ancient text is such an idea!"

Both doctors, both heads of the School of Surgery, had risen. It was a sign that the interview was over. "We cannot dare subject our students, much less our patients, to heresy," said Dr. Brunswick.

A kind of dispassionate anger flared into Paracelsus' mind; he was at the point of scorching their ears, not with any personal abuse, but with a furor against traditional ignorance. He knew that his outbursts infuriated other doctors, even excellent ones; but his own ideals were too high, and the practice of the overwhelming majority of doctors too low for him to care. But Vendelinus Hock, rejoining the group from the window, spoke first.

"Perhaps Paracelsus would not mind meeting our students in the morning," he said to his colleagues, who looked at him stonily. He ignored their silence and said to Paracelsus: "We're meeting in assembly on the green."

The next morning Paracelsus sat on a platform with the other three, all of them in academic robes. Were they, then, accepting him? He did not know. Dr. Hock, behind the speaker's lectern, had introduced him as the new "knight-errant in the world of medicine" who was even now "on a crusade of his own." The doctor mentioned the age-old practice of administering spirits to lessen the shock of amputation. "Not so, Paracelsus," he intoned dryly. "Our Paracelsus has a better way."

He mentioned the technique, tried and proven, of covering the wound with a salve which would bring forth the healing pus. "Not so, Paracelsus," he said even more dryly. "Our Paracelsus has a better way.

One by one, he mentioned all the suggestions which Paracelsus had made the day before, his sarcasm becoming more and more apparent, the students, who knew his wit was keener than his scalpel, were tittering and laughing. By the time Dr. Hock had ended his introduction, ridiculing the idea that an infection could be cured "from within" and suggesting that the knight-errant should first take his course in dissection so that he would, on looking "within," know what to expect—the laughter of the students had risen to a roar.

Dr. Vendelinus Hock, raising his arms, quieted the students. "Surgeons of tomorrow," he said, "I give you Paracelsus!"

Paracelsus did not go behind the lectern; he went in front of it. And there, in full view of his audience, he simply let the professor's robe slip from his shoulders to the floor. Then he walked into the crowd. Silently, they gave way; but as he passed they began to jeer. Paracelsus had not taken up the challenge. By the time he had cleared the crowd, the students had hoisted their champion, Dr. Hock, onto their shoulders and, cheering, were carrying him in triumph across the green.

Paracelsus went directly to his new quarters to pack: Strasbourg was not for him after all. At his door he found a messenger impatiently waiting for him with an urgent call—a call which, by a remarkable coincidence, would not only dramatically vindicate his claim that serious infections could be cured from within, but would bring him fame.

9

SEVENTY MILES FROM STRASBOURG, in Basel, a man named Froben was critically ill of an infected leg. He had written to Paracelsus. "Eight doctors, all of them men of talent, sing the same song. 'The leg must go.' But when the leg goes, Froben goes. I will not live without my walks in the country. Does Paracelsus know a better way?" The tone of the note pleased Paracelsus, and he looked again at the signature: Froben. Didn't he know that name?

Hurriedly, he scrawled a note: "Clean the body thoroughly, outside and in," and ordered an emetic to be followed within the hour by an enema. "Go quickly," he said, handing the messenger the note. "Say 'Paracelsus follows hard behind.'"

He had exchanged three horses, galloping across the countryside, when he remembered who this Froben was. He drew his horse up sharply and said aloud, "Johann Froben! Froben the publisher!"

Publisher indeed. Johann Froben was the foremost pub-

lisher in Europe. In himself he had no special claim to
fame, but he was the most intimate friend of the most
cultured and, intellectually, the most powerful figure of
the day, a man universally regarded as the "prince of the
humanists"—Desiderius Erasmus. Erasmus, whose book *In
Praise of Folly* had made him the prime figure in the re-
birth of learning; Erasmus, whose new translation, from
Greek into Latin, of the New Testament had shaken the
accepted version; Erasmus, whose letters were the prizes
of all the kings in Europe: to this man, Johann Froben was
both business partner and boon companion. Although Froben's was a reflected glory, a glory it nevertheless was, and
on his plight was turned the attention of every scholar and
professor, every king and courtier in Europe. When the
realization came to Paracelsus, he laughed aloud.

On the evening of the second day after he received the
message, Paracelsus walked through the street room with
the giant new press, its grooved and greasy spindle two
inches across, to Froben's quarters in the rear. There on a
luxurious bed, sitting three-quarters up, was a round-faced
man who, Paracelsus knew at a glance, could be stubborn
or jolly as the mood came. The right leg, swathed in bandages, was thrust stiffly ahead and rested upon a huge pillow. A servant stood by with water, soap and a towel and,
without speaking, Paracelsus washed his hands and arms.

"The odor coming from the kitchen is very rich," he
said as he dried his hands.

"Our dinner for tonight, Herr Doctor," said Froben
happily. Froben was always happy when he talked about
food. Paracelsus had already moved to the bedside and
had pressed a finger into the soft tissue of the good ankle.

"A special stew," Froben went on. "Rare cut of veal,

six spices delicately balanced, seasoned with three kinds
of wine. You'll love it, Paracelsus, take my word."

"I'll love it, Johann. But not you. You'll dine on roots
and leaves for a week or two." With quick, careful strokes
of his scissors, he was cutting the bandages away as Froben reached for his glass of spiced hot wine. Paracelsus,
as if absent-mindedly, intercepted it.

"Your master will be having water. Much as he pleases.
Neither cold nor warm," he said, as he examined the infected limb. The leg, from the middle of the shin to the
toes, seemed blown up from the inside. The skin was a
design of mottled patterns, gray and blue around the leak-
ing, pus-filled abscess on the inside of the lower calf, pink
and white and shiny as it joined the healthier skin. It was
touch and go with the leg; Paracelsus could certainly understand the other doctors' *consilium.* He looked hard at
Froben: the key was there, with him. Did he want to recover? Would he obey absolutely? Was he strong enough,
not for a quick amputation with its certain results (whatever the psychic scar afterward), but for a monthlong
grind of spartan habits?

"How badly do you want the leg?" said Paracelsus.

"As much as breath itself."

"That is easy to say."

Froben had had enough. He was in no mood for an insult, however veiled. "Is this your vaunted method, Paracelsus?" he bellowed. "Do you propose to insult me back
to health?"

The display of spirit pleased Paracelsus. "Your anger is
excellent, Johann," he said mildly, "but only if you direct
it at yourself. Both legs are gouty. The infected leg has
had too many doctors, too many cures. The muscles are
good, praise God—your walks in the country. But we must

change the alchemy of the blood. It is not the leg we heal. It is the entire body. It is Johann. New basic foods. New basic fluids—juices, herbal teas and broths. Fresh air and sun. New color, new rhythm, new life."

"And if I do all this," said Froben, subdued a little, "what can you guarantee?"

Paracelsus did not answer. He went over to his satchel and slipped the scissors in their place. "Two months from now, at Einsiedeln," he said reminiscently, "the edelweiss will bloom."

"Here, too," said Johann Froben, pleased at the thought.

"It will be thrilling picking them up there, a mile high," said Paracelsus.

"Ahh," said Froben sadly. "Pick some for me."

"Pick them yourself, Johann," said Paracelsus. "Pick them two months from now—yourself."

Froben grinned, his face radiating a great joy. In his mind Paracelsus knew that, unless he, the doctor in the case, proved stupid, the patient was already cured. The rest was a matter of time.

"I make bold to greet the new city doctor of Basel," came a voice from behind him, a voice carefully correct.

"No, sir. Paracelsus von Hohenheim."

"And with the first step Froben takes, new city doctor," said the mild-mannered newcomer. He was soberly dressed, a long, dark smock over a yellow shirt with a ruffled collar, this on a slight frame. Everything about the man, Paracelsus noted, was studied—the gestures, the walk as he approached, the suggestion of a smile, even the yellow collar and the long, carefully combed blond hair. And yet he carried this study with a lightness and a grace that could, Paracelsus knew, only belong to one man: Erasmus of Rotterdam.

"Erasmus knows something which I do not," said Paracelsus, deftly concluding the introductions.

"It is such a pleasure these days to bear good news," said Erasmus with a thin but mirthful laugh. "But it's quite true. If Froben walks again—and if you choose—the position not only of the city doctor of Basel but also of professor of medicine at the university is yours."

And Erasmus went on, speaking naturally in carefully balanced sentences spiced occasionally with quotes from the Greek, to explain local politics which made for the opening. The present town doctor, a Herr Professor Wonecker, had accepted miserable conditions as human failings, going along with the status quo; and now, in his doddering old age, had insulted the Reformation leaders in a Protestant city. The city fathers were vaguely aware of Paracelsus' views, and had the impression—a correct one—that although he was profoundly spiritual he was irreligious. This aspect did not please them mightily, but he seemed to occupy a sort of middle ground which might soothe the rival factions; and his reputation, especially if he cured Froben, would bring to the city a certain liberal and progressive air. They wanted him. "And for our part," Erasmus, using the royal "we," said "we want no less."

These two most brilliant figures of the day sitting opposite each other at the foot of Froben's bed, sizing each other up as they exchanged views about the extraordinary times in which they lived.

They agreed on one basic idea: that it was only the individual, and not a group, that mattered; and as a consequence, both the established Church and the rabid, new Lutherans, as groups, were blind forces. Erasmus was passively, Paracelsus actively, neutral. But in most other ways the two were opposites, poles of the same magnet, and

Froben, propped on his wide, plush pillow, forgot his leg as he contemplated them.

Erasmus walked and talked as quietly as possible, as if he dreaded that the quiet would be broken by some boorish joke or peasant laughter. Paracelsus was quiet itself, but his words, once he started, jutted upwards in a torrent of intuition. Erasmus glowed when he made a distinction, Paracelsus when he found the right metaphor. Erasmus wore clothes impeccably laundered and pressed and arranged; Paracelsus slept in his clothes until they were too dirty for his patients to abide, and then he exchanged the old for a brand new outfit, giving the soiled one to the first poor man who came his way. The dour scholar had given his life to books, ancient and new; the mystic physician insisted that the only book worth a wise man's time was the book of nature, which must be studied by experiment. So it was no surprise that the conversation sputtered.

Erasmus was secretly astonished that this boyish and poetical doctor, who spoke so directly and even crudely, could cure so much as a mild itch, though he did not doubt it; and Paracelsus wondered how a man so highly reputed could content himself with the ironical meanderings of the mere reason. But when the conversation was over, both rose with a feeling of respect. They were like two whales who, used to making a straight path through schools of small fry, were obliged to alter course just the slightest bit to veer around each other.

"I leave you with a gift which is a warning," said Erasmus, with a thin smile. "You will not fare well with the academic mind."

Paracelsus laughed merrily. "You know already what I have learned at great length and great pain!" Then, soberly, he added, "You do not fare better with your liver."

Erasmus laughed at the display of wit and then, seeing that Paracelsus was in dead earnest, stopped short. His left hand, in the first unconscious gesture of the encounter, came up and rested at the stomach.

"The liver, Paracelsus? Are you certain?"

"There are signs."

"More of this when we have greater leisure," said the prince of the humanists. He bowed and went out.

Already the word was out: Paracelsus had taken on Froben as a patient. Indeed, the news was like a stone dropped into water, it spread like waves, taking on circle after circle, academies and guilds and courts. All Basel knew within the hour; by the end of the next day the countryside for a hundred miles around, including Strasbourg, knew; and by the end of the week, the whole of Europe. Doctors especially took notice. Besides the few who respected this "Luther of medicine," there were many who, foreseeing still another successful cure, grew grim; but most, at their next guild meetings, were beside themselves with glee. Everybody had known for a month that the Froben leg was a cistern of contagion. They knew too that Froben was a stubborn and impatient man who would not abide much discipline and that, without immediate amputation, he could not survive more than a week or two. And death of so celebrated a figure would, at long last, crush the mountebank healer once and for all.

The mountebank, meantime, was hard at work.

When Paracelsus undertook a cure, he spared neither the patient nor himself. The hour for self-indulgence was past; now was the hour of law. He shouldered the patient's burdens as his own. He lost no chance to bring about positive changes, not only in physical habits but in the mental stance as well.

First, he moved Johann from the sagging, overluxurious bed to a simple one with a straw mattress; he himself slept on the floor. Next, he cleared the body of the excessively rich foods, using fairly harsh, then milder laxatives and enemas; and excused himself to his patient, explaining that he had decided to take the opportunity to "reconstitute himself." The two, doctor and patient, shared the same simple foods, which stressed "theriac," a special Paracelsan mixture including vinegar and honey, and cherry juice. He treated the wound sparingly; but he himself massaged the healthier parts of the leg, working lower and lower into the inflamed portion and after the massage, supervised the gentle exercises—the tightening of muscle, the moving of the toes—which, he explained, was coaxing back the "archaeus," or life force into the diseased parts.

All the while, he watched Johann's mental state like a hawk. When Froben from time to time doubted the effectiveness of a tiny, bitter pill, he would repair to his sword which was always in view. There, he would unscrew the hollow pommel and gently shake out the powder, the most potent medicine in the world, into a glass of water, and hand his patient the clear, tasteless drink to wash down the pill. When Froben's nerves were ready to snap, Paracelsus changed the scene, the mood, the medication completely. He had brought in an entire crock of the raw, unsweetened wine which both proceeded to drink; he brought in galleys of a new work for him to correct; and once he brought in an accomplished and handsome actress from a traveling troupe to play the lute and to sing.

Five days passed with mounting tension and no apparent results, and then the leg responded dramatically.

The swelling reduced by a third. The wholesome area of the skin covered another two inches of the calf. The ulcerous opening itself ripened into a well-defined, though still pus-filled, abscess. For the first time in six weeks Johann dared set the sole of the foot to the floor. On the thirtieth day after Paracelsus' arrival, Johann Froben, leaning on a cane, was seen plucking a bouquet of lilies from his garden. Not only was the leg decidedly on the road to recovery, but he himself, by his own word, had never felt better in his life.

And even as Erasmus had predicted, the very next morning a Sebastian Amerbach, wealthy merchant and city alderman, appeared at Froben's door: would the esteemed doctor of both medicines consent to serve in the combined position of city doctor and professor of medicine at the University of Basel? Paracelsus would, he said, and gladly. Herr Amerbach, stuffy with office but goodhearted, grinned. "And when," he said, "could the renowned physician start?"

Paracelsus picked up his broad-brimmed teamster's hat. "Is now soon enough?"

Outside, the polished official carriage waited, and in it Alderman Amerbach drove the new city doctor to his office on the University of Basel campus. So here it was, thought Paracelsus, with a feeling of intense well-being. A job to answer his dreams, and in the land of his birth! The air, the mountains, the buildings seemed beautiful. And between himself and Sebastian there was a genuine affection. Beneath the officious air was a simple soul, thought Paracelsus; and he knew that Sebastian appreciated his own sympathy with the downtrodden and the poor. But the sense of well-being was soon to go. When Sebastian drew up to the university, there were a dozen horses stomping at the posts, and with an air of surprise he said, "There seems to be a meeting . . . !"

Inside, in the ample room allocated to the city doctor, waited a cluster of men in professorial robes. Alderman Sebastian and Paracelsus, obviously, were expected. A venerable man, who identified himself as the dean, stepped forward and, addressing Sebastian, stated coldly: "The new professor of medicine will be obliged to pass the colloquy."

"But it is mere formality," said Sebastian, taken aback. "The appointment has been made and approved."

"By the aldermen, perhaps," said the dean, "but not by the faculty."

"Are you talkers here, or healers?" said Paracelsus good-humoredly. The colloquy was another of the tiresome debates, really a last-ditch measure to prevent undesirables from attaining a status equal to themselves. "My colloquy in Basel is Johann Froben."

"Nevertheless, sir," sputtered the dean, "nevertheless you must debate a champion of our choosing." The old man motioned to his right, and out from the group stepped a familiar figure. Paracelsus could not believe his eyes: it was none other than the victor of the Strasbourg debate, Vendelinus Hock.

"Herr Amerbach," said Paracelsus, "is the position mine?"

"The post of city doctor and of professor are yours."

"It is enough," said Paracelsus. And for the second time in a matter of weeks, he turned his back on the sharp-tongued master of words, Dr. Hock.

What followed was a series of moves in a game which Paracelsus thoroughly enjoyed. That is to say, the university officials played the game and Paracelsus either changed the rules or ignored them. For, he reasoned, what were their rules to him? They had showed their bad faith, had exchanged mere conventions for honor and, hypocritically, expected him to act the part of an honorable man. They deserved either contempt or humor, and humor was more fun. So as the dean, in the name of the faculty, made official demands, Paracelsus openly twitted him. The dean demanded to see his credentials; Paracelsus, although he had received a Master of Arts diploma from Ferrara, scorned to use it. He sent instead a list of names of patients whom he had healed and included, with permission, an excerpt of a letter from Erasmus which read:

To Theophrastus, the highly expert doctor of Medicine, Erasmus sends his greetings. . . . I am amazed to see how well you know me to the marrow although you saw me only once. I know the riddles in which you speak are verily true. . . . I cannot offer any compensation adequate to your art, but I promise to bear gratitude toward you. You have brought back from hell, Froben, who is my other half. If you restore my health, too, you will give us back to each other. Let Fortune retain you in Basel.

The dean, issuing a written challenge to Paracelsus, held the colloquy, evidently expecting to anger "the mountebank" into debating; Paracelsus simply didn't show up. In the name of the faculty the dean required Paracelsus to submit a program of his intended course and Paracelsus thought the program an excellent idea. He carefully composed one and ran off copies on the Froben press. But instead of submitting it to the faculty, he personally passed out sheets not only to "qualified" university students but to lowly barber-surgeons and midwives, to herbalists and bathhouse attendants. The program flaunted the study of ancient texts "slavishly," stating that "this way may lead to splendid titles, but does not make a true doctor. What a doctor needs," the program went on, "is not eloquence or knowledge of language and of books, illustrious though they be, but profound knowledge of Nature and her works."

He would teach his own healing methods—pathology, therapeutics, pharmacology, diagnosis, purgation, venesection—which were not another vapid compilation of excerpts from the ancients. Of his methods, he said, "In ceaseless toil I created them anew upon the foundation of experience, the supreme teacher of all things." And then, almost incidentally, he gave a new direction to medicine, one which three and a half centuries later would be coming into its own: "If I want to prove anything I shall not do so by quoting authorities, but by experiment and by reasoning thereupon."

The gall of this man, said the professors. In one breath he insults his contemporaries and dares state that the revered ancients, whose words have come down unchanged through fifteen centuries, had not said the final word. Every thinking professor of the university was outraged. They united and issued a new decree, this one to the students: no one who registered for Paracelsus' new course would be allowed to take the examinations, none who in any way consorted with him would graduate.

But the academic outrage was soon to turn to cold fury. The number of "qualified" students who registered, compared with the number enrolled the year before, quadrupled, and the "uneducated" proudly signed their names or left their marks by the dozens. The university officials were forced to play their last, and trump, card—and this, on the opening day of the new class. One by one the students gathered before the door of Paracelsus' office on campus, where the class was to be held, but they found the door locked and the lock changed. Paracelsus arrived, discovered the new gambit and, grinning at the resourcefulness of his enemies, addressed the crowd. He would hire his own hall and meet them in a week.

And so, one week later to the hour, in a hall just off campus, a crowd far greater than that of a week before—for the eyes of the city were on the man who was fighting the fusty deadheads single-handedly—faced a scene never before witnessed in a classroom. The usual lectern was not there. Before the benches were an alchemist's oven, already fired, and a long, sturdy table cluttered with alembics and retorts, with crucibles and pelicans—metalware and glassware in a tangle of forms. They waited with an air of excitement and, as they eyed the mysterious apparatus, of fear.

Paracelsus' entrance was a distinct disappointment. He walked in as officiously and as stiffly as any professor. Not only did he wear the long, black robe and the flat cap, but he carried in an enormous tome—Galen, and even carried the reciting rod. Imperiously, he marched to the center of the table; and there, with an attitude of great deliberation, examined the volume of Galen. But then he set it on a low stool and sat upon it. Still solemnly, he snapped the rod and tossed the pieces over his shoulder, behind him.

Then, grasping the black robe at the neck, one hand to each side, he ripped it apart, carefully, at the seams and consigned both sides to the flames of the athanor. And finally, still with extreme propriety, he removed the flat cap and mopped up a puddle of water on the table. A few of the bolder souls in the audience had tittered when he sat on the Galen, but by the time he had mopped the table with the professional cap, the whole audience was howling. And when he stood, the battered old alchemist's jacket in full view, the laughter was mixed with cheers. For a full five minutes the students and the riffraff cheered. At last, at last there was a professor on campus—or, rather, just off campus—who was *alive*. And indeed, no one laughed louder or more deeply than Paracelsus himself. He was in his element.

The crowd was still relishing the joke as he and his new attendant, a young man called Oporinus who had attached himself to "the magician," set to work. Oporinus brought the fire to a white heat and moved a brazier of hot coals to the center of the table. Paracelsus, separating the apparatus in two, apparently for two separate demonstrations, was handling each piece of equipment with the hands of a master. The class was now so quiet the least clink of glass on glass carried throughout the room. Without ado, Paracelsus began to speak.

"The end of alchemy is not to change lead into gold. The end of alchemy is to find new ways to heal." Again, to Paracelsus' surprise, the crowd started to cheer. And then he understood. He was lecturing not in learned Latin, but in street German. He was not dressing up a simple idea into ambiguity, he was making a complex thought as simple as he could. He resumed his talk, and the voices faded away into intense silence.

Paracelsus held up two jars, both of which contained a black, metallic powder. "To an ordinary man, unlearned in alchemy," he said, and added impishly, "a professor or a doctor," as the audience laughed, "to the ordinary man, these are the same. They appear the same, they smell and taste the same. But they are as different as night and day. This one," he said, holding high the bottle in his right hand, "has power to change iron into copper." A murmur of wonder passed over the crowd. "And this," he said, raising the left, "contains in it a Martian 'chaos.'"

The students, their timidity and distrust overcome, edged near the worktable. They wanted to miss nothing. They watched and listened as Paracelsus experimented with the first powder. They saw him heat it, with no extraordinary effect. Then they saw it turn into blue vitriol as he poured the oil of vitriol into the retort. He took a few of the crystals so formed and, dissolving them into a vat, asked for any piece of iron from the crowd. Reluctantly, a bath attendant from the rear passed up an iron dagger. The dagger Paracelsus suspended from the hilt down into the blue fluid. It was to stay awhile, Paracelsus explained, until the virtue had a chance to work.

As Paracelsus brought the retort containing the second powder to the coals, there was an immediate reaction. The powder decomposed, and a lazy, reddish-brown or "Martian" gas or "chaos" formed over the residue.

The crowd was fascinated. Paracelsus explained that much which was called magic was called rightfully so, but in a sense completely different from that which inquisitions or academies understood by the word. All minerals and all plants had such magical properties; but instead of trying them first in the fire and then, intelligently and in correct dosages, in living things, those who called themselves "teachers" were wasting time and energy and life repeating the blunders of centuries. He began to introduce his new chemistry, one based upon the three basic elements of sulphur, mercury and salt, when the time was up.

"Come get your dagger, Otto," he said to the masseur. Sure enough, the gray blade was everywhere a lustrous, dull orange. "Much too beautiful to be used, eh, Otto?"

he said, to the astonished man. And Otto walked away, stroking the glistening blade.

The course was a success beyond Paracelsus' dreams. Students who had no interest in medicine or alchemy dropped in to see "his latest trick" and hear his latest jibe at the professors next door "in limbo." And he discouraged no man from learning according to his interest and capacity. In return, his students gradually came to look to him as a leader. Where they refused to "follow the stick" like good boys, memorizing their classics only to spew them back at the appointed hour, they eagerly accepted the new formula of experiment and reason. In fact, so impelling was his attraction to many students that he was obliged to channel their rebellion, to distinguish for them between empty tradition and insufferable convention on the one hand, and *law*, the obligation of each man for his fellows and himself, on the other. But at the moment, academic rebellion had in it more of truth than academic orthodoxy, and so they rebelled.

The traditional day of rebellion for students was St. John's day, when after a day of mildly destructive antics, they built a fire in the middle of the campus green. Into this fire they threw police clubs, professors' hats and canes, an occasional habit of a priest or a nun—anything which symbolized their irritations. When the fire was at its most dramatic and intense, they would bring in two or three effigies, always of the dreariest teachers, and burn them; and it would take at least two weeks for the secret snickers to subside into intellectual death.

But the excitement of St. John's day, 1527, was to last for several generations. For when the fire had reached its peak, a man in an alchemist's jacket came through the night wheeling an enormous book in a wheelbarrow. The book was Avicenna's *Summa,* the Bible of the medical texts of the day; the man was Paracelsus.

The noisy students, sensing what was to follow, grew serious. Men, they well knew, had been burned at the stake for less. Nevertheless, as Paracelsus struggled to unload the giant tome from the humble conveyance, four leaped forward to give him a hand. As Paracelsus counted, the students heaved. For a moment Avicenna resisted the flame; and then the covers burst open with a pop and the pages never crackled with a livelier sound. As the students cheered, Paracelsus, with the mock incantation of the Pope at High Mass, pronounced: "The realm of the sacred art of medicine do I thus purge!"

But as the flames of the fire died, so died Paracelsus' one moment of glory among the world of men.

10

I T WAS NOT that Paracelsus did not succeed. He succeeded too often and too well. As his class continued to thrive, it also continued to show clearly and dramatically that traditional medicine was a compilation of brilliant half-truths and outrageous blunders. And this made enemies for him. As he tackled the various duties of city doctor, he was obliged to oppose practices common not only to men whose job it was to heal—the doctors, the pharmacists, the barber-surgeons and bath attendants, but to other tradesmen—the vintners, the greengrocers and butchers. And this made enemies for him, too. In a very real sense, he was one man opposing a world. Even his friends who did not understand his intent perfectly were apt to become a trial for him. And one of these friends was none other than Johann Froben.

Once healed, Johann forgot about the edelweiss blooming in the mountains. It seemed to him that he had stared into the hollow eyes of death, and he decided that now he wanted to *live*. But curiously, where before the infected leg he was a reasonably moral man, now his idea of "life" was out-and-out pleasure. No idle gloss in one of his books was the saying, "Eat, drink and make merry, for tomorrow ye may die"; it was his new way of life. Even so, Johann Froben was neither an ingrate nor a fool. Once a month, partly out of gratitude and partly to stay under his doctor's eye, he invited Paracelsus to a Sunday dinner.

Over and over the same scene would take place.

"Eat, Theophrastus," Johann would say. "Flesh is not immortal, it wants feeding. Even a magician's, like yourself. So eat!" On a giant prong he would be holding a leg of lamb just under Paracelsus' nose.

And resisting his jollity, Paracelsus would cut off a modest slice and return the shank. "Too much, Johann, too much," he would murmur. "You're getting heavier than a cow."

On the defensive, Johann would try to turn the warning into banter. "Aha!" he would say. "At last I've caught you in a lie. Yes, by the blood of Christ, you're wrong. You have the gender wrong. Maybe 'as heavy as a bull,' but not a cow!"

Paracelsus would refuse the byplay. He would eat sullenly, knowing full well how vain it was, but still hoping to impress his friend with the seriousness of his failing. But then, as the wine flowed, he too would become cheerful.

After an hour of gossip and fun, Johann, with a great show of duty, would push himself away from the table and get his own, and Paracelsus' hat. It was time for the constitutional, the mile walk prescribed for Johann after every evening meal. Once in the country, the two would walk in utter quiet among the fields, the trees, the tiny signs of life, as if breathing in the changing light of dusk.

On one of these walks they had scarcely made the outskirts of town when Froben, gasping, stumbled over to a stump. Sitting stiffly, he extended a leg—the left one this time—and clutched the knee, trying to choke back the pain below.

"What is it, Paracelsus?" he said between clenched teeth. "What can it be?"

Paracelsus' voice was icy. "A sharp throb rising from the ankle. A knife of fire inside, that cuts and burns. Comes suddenly and leaves the same. Meantime, the joints get pale and puffy. Suppose you tell me what it is, Johann? You know only too well."

"One does not die of gout," said Johann resentfully. He was still rebelling inside.

"One dies from the *cause* of gout!" said Paracelsus, overwhelming him into silence. Then, thinking that for such men as Froben pain was the best advice, he spoke affectionately again. "Mind your Hippocrates, Johann: 'Fat men die suddenly.'"

Johann was straightening out his leg again. The throb of pain was gone, but his thoughts were still dark.

"You, his severest critic, quote Hippocrates?" he said petulantly.

"His errors I criticize," said Paracelsus with a chuckle. "His truth I steal."

Both men laughed freely then, and something of the mood of serenity returned. They walked on.

"I have an idea," Johann said, stopping in his tracks. "I have an inspiration! What do you say we go, the two of us, to the Zurich Fair? It'll be a change for you, and a grand farewell to my old way of life for me. What do you say?"

Shaking his head and smiling, Paracelsus shook a thumb over his shoulder, back in the direction of the stump. "I thought you made your last farewell back there," he said.

Abashed, Johann Froben for the hundredth time swore off the good life. He would hold firm for a day or two. And then the smell of apple strudel, fresh-baked, or the hiss of a beer frothing over a tankard, or the sight of a nubile maid pulling the milk out of a cow's udder would whet his appetite for "just one more" taste of "life."

Much as Paracelsus enjoyed friends, he never sought them. Indeed, he avoided a social life. The very idea of society seemed to him a lie, and he deliberately cultivated crude manners and plain-spoken outcasts. He had given it considerable thought and had decided that the high society of his day needed a purge, and he would be among those few who purged it. But the few individuals, usually of very high station or of very low, whom life had made his friends he trusted absolutely.

Characteristically for him, he put complete trust in the members of his class. These young men had taken to his teachings with such fervor that he felt sure his dream of founding a new medicine, and a new breed of men to practice it, was coming true. They galvanized his own mind into new channels by flooding him with questions, by proposing new, alternative theories; a half dozen of them set up chemical laboratories of their own. The two-hour class lasted four hours and longer, until some experiment or other was complete. Even past the hour of the evening meal there remained a handful; and—an amazing fact to Paracelsus—the last to go was always Johann Herbst, who called himself "Oporinus."

Oporinus seemed to be a sly, critical sort. From the beginning Paracelsus expected him to attend a few classes, enough to form a quick, negative opinion, and leave. But to his continuing surprise, Oporinus seldom missed a class. And he always stayed afterward. Not only did he appoint himself assistant, but he attended faithfully to all details— to the fire, the calcination, the distillation, his sidelong glances never missing the least movement of Paracelsus' hands. Indeed, Oporinus occasionally made a nuisance of himself through, apparently, his absolute dedication. The experiment of "changing iron into copper" he repeated several times, each time wheedling Paracelsus into explaining every detail. They were finishing an experiment late one afternoon when Paracelsus heard his assistant whisper, "Don't look now, Master Paracelsus, but the bearded one . . ."

Paracelsus looked up. The hall was empty save for two students seated and a third standing. "Leaning against the column?" he said, in a normal tone of voice.

Oporinus, irritated, waited before answering, again in a whisper. "Yes. He's spying on you."

The absurd statement affected Paracelsus strangely. Months back he had himself noticed the mysterious listener who always stood, arms crossed, leaning on the same post, never asking a question and never answering. Paracelsus' classes were open and they would remain so: it was his way. But something about the man suggested to him that he came to observe and to report to some person or some group, that he received instructions and then returned to listen again. Ever since Vendelinus Hock had materialized so unexpectedly on the university campus— for it was unheard of, that the faculty of one campus would hire an outsider to do their arguing for them—ever since, a dark seed had been stirring in his mind. And now, with Oporinus' remark, the dark idea and the bearded listener became one: he, Paracelsus, was a marked man.

"Why would he spy on me?" he whispered to Oporinus, hoping for a clue as to who sent the "spy."

"Why, master . . ." said Oporinus, hinting darkly at something. "Because you *know*."

"I know what, Oporinus?"

Oporinus shrugged. "About the stone. The *stone*." Oporinus had convinced himself that his master could change lead into gold.

"About the bladder stones I know a little."

"Just as you say," said Oporinus, grinning wisely.

"Only fools cook metals to make gold. Wise men cook metals to make new medicines."

"It's as the master says." Oporinus was grinning all the more broadly, as if Paracelsus had included him in on a piece of very dry wit. But looking at the suspicious eyes, the mirthless grin, the furtive air, Paracelsus was merely infuriated. And then, remembering himself and remembering, too, Oporinus' fidelity and efficiency, he curbed his tongue. Oporinus, it was clear, knew nothing useful about the "spy." Certainly he did not know who had sent him. Deliberately, Paracelsus looked hard at the bearded man and he, suddenly ill at ease under Paracelsus' glance, drifted away.

Quite by accident Paracelsus himself, when he was making one of his routine inspections, discovered who had hired the bearded one to observe his actions.

An old city ordinance, never exercised until now, assigned the city doctor the duty of inspecting pharmacies, barbershops and bathhouses—those facilities which directly affected public health. And to the consternation of many tradespeople, he took the ordinance literally. With the barbers and the masseurs at the baths, he had no trouble. They were for the most part simple folk, and he spoke their language. Willingly or grudgingly, they adopted the changes which he proposed—the curb on bloodletting in the barbershops, the building of special pools in the baths for the leprous and the ulcerated. But the pharmacists, who had risen high and fast in the social scale, were another matter altogether.

Every pharmacist in Basel had begun as a greengrocer. Herbs were, after all, vegetable greens, fresh or powdered or rolled into pills, and every enterprising greengrocer was sure to have an herb concession on the side. But soon the shrewd, and often the unscrupulous, grocer discovered that the big money was not in the spinach but in the "spirits Universalis," not in the produce but in the pills. So all over town as the vegetable stalls dwindled in number and size, the shelves with the mysterious bottles and sachets and boxes expanded and grew, until at last there were a dozen pharmacies around town which sold no spinach at all.

Moreover, the more aggressive grocers-become-pharmacists discovered that added dividends were theirs for the asking if on occasion they consented to play doctor. Doctors came high in Basel; and whenever there was some "nameless little complaint" going the rounds, a smart burger could save himself a good piece of change by cutting out the doctor and taking his advice directly from the druggist. The druggist would know the medication and the dosage anyway.

Besides, there was always time, when the patient went from bad to worse, to send for the doctor (or the doctor's assistant, since only the rare doctor made house calls).

And the extraordinarily gifted druggist went one step
farther. Finding himself a middleman between the patient
and the doctor, it occurred to him that this middle
could fatten by feeding from both ends. By cutting the
doctor in on a generous share of his profits, he could make
it clear that the more "exclusive preparations" which the
doctor found convenient to swing his way, the greater the
profit for both. For instance, he might be asked to prepare
this typical "recipe":

Gold, one half ounce, Powder of a lion's heart, four ounces. Filings
of a unicorn's horn, one half ounce, Ashes of the whole chameleon, one
and a half ounces. Bark of witch hazel, two handfuls. Earthworms, a
score. Dried man's brain, five ounces. Bruisewort and Egyptian onions
of each one half pound. Mix the ingredients together and digest in
spirits Universalis, with a warm digestion, from the change of the
moon to the full, and pass through a fine strain.

All this, of course, would be prescribed in Latin. It was
unfitting that the vulgar should become acquainted with
any secret of the divine art; and besides, the Latin for
"witch hazel," say, always commanded a better price than
the straight Swiss, especially with a whole wood of it
growing just outside town. If the pharmacist found himself
fresh out of unicorn's horn, he might reasonably substitute
the filings of a sow's tooth, and chameleons are enough
like tadpoles for the latter to work just as well. Who
would know? Certainly not the physician, whose hands
were not to be soiled with such foul medications. And he
was getting his cut anyway. Predictably, it was these greengrocers turned pharmacists who, along with the doctors
hidebound by tradition, opposed Paracelsus most resolutely.

He was making a random inspection of Suder's
pharmacy, the largest in Basel, when he walked into a
meeting of several guilds. He had not been expected;

indeed, his appearance at the door seemed to have an electric effect not only on the speaker, who stopped in the middle of a sentence, but on the entire assembly. Row after row turned to see who was standing in the doorway. Nothing further was said; the meeting was adjourned. But there was no question in Paracelsus' mind as to what, or who, had been the subject of the meeting. He was. And standing there as the guild members filed past, he learned through the silence the alarming extent of his enemies and the amazing number of his friends who seemed other than they were. It was at this guild meeting that he saw the bearded one, the "spy," in a deep conversation with three men dressed in the official doctor robes. He was not surprised.

What by turns surprised and alarmed and amused him was that so formidable an opposition should have formed against one man. Harassment had by now become his lot and, although it never failed to move him deeply, he had resigned himself to it. But the harassment had always been limited to the sniping of individuals or, at most, a town council.

There had been the unsigned letters, the veiled denunciations, the public proclamations. More recently there had been lampoons. One by a Valentinus ab Riso set out to satirize Paracelsus' accomplishments and industry, referring to "two hundred and thirty books on philosophy, forty on medicine, twelve on government, seven on mathematics and astrology and sixty-six about secret and magic arts" which he purportedly had written. But the intended victim turned out the victor. It was as if the satirist were unaware of his own latent admiration for Paracelsus.

A second lampoon hit the mark. It was addressed to "Cacophrastus," a scabrous play on Paracelsus' first name, and written by "the ghost of Galen" rising from the grave. The ghost prescribes for his detractor the herb hellebore, which was used for mental disturbances; and after evaluating Paracelsus' contribution to medicine, concludes:

> You are not worthy of carrying Hippocrates' chamber pot,
> Or to feed my swine.

The ghost proceeds to ridicule Paracelsus' new approach, calling his medications "mad, alchemical vaporings," accuses Paracelsus on the one hand of dodging Vendelinus' "well-reasoned word" and on the other of winning his fame through his "cunning tongue." It ends on a blunt note of foreboding:

> What will you do, madman, when you are found out?
> I suggest you hang yourself.

At the same time, his class was disrupted in various ways. Hired hecklers interrupted the lectures. Students were threatened. On several occasions, expensive retorts and pelicans—the glass equipment—were broken. But all this Paracelsus endured, for he had no doubt that the city fathers would restore order in due course.

Soon, however, he had reason to believe that he no longer enjoyed the good graces of these august gentlemen. All that was needed to put an end to these irritations, he thought, was a simple statement by the aldermen, made publicly, that he, Paracelsus, was their choice and that they supported him. They had promised him no less. So he wrote an urgent letter asking for this vote of confidence and requiring, as a minimum for doing a reasonably good job, two powers. First, he expected to be entitled "to graduate my disciples to be doctors as behooves a full professor"; and he insisted that the old ordinance on the inspection of pharmacies be strictly enforced, specifically mentioning "abuses which are doing great damage" and pharmacists acting "in collusion with" doctors to fatten each other's fees. This urgent letter the fathers, budding bureaucrats that they were, consigned to the slow, certain death of inanition: they simply filed it away and "forgot" about it.

The situation now was a most remarkable one. Every petty official from the burgomeister down, every guild officer and virtually every "professional" man, wanted Paracelsus out immediately and under any circumstances. He was an offense to empowered ignorance—and he was bad for business. And just as fervently, a few of the men of position and all of the common people wanted him to stay. As a result of this balance of forces, although the resistance was solidly formed, its leaders did not as yet dare to move into the open. Impatiently, they waited for Paracelsus to blunder—to blunder conspicuously enough for them to create a cause. Month after long month they waited—in vain. At last they hit upon a stratagem which would serve them even better than a blunder, which would set a trap.

A Cornelius von Liechtenfels, a canon in the Catholic Church whose dislike for Paracelsus was intense, was grievously ill of the "English sweat." For some weeks, signs of the disorder seemed about to disappear when they would return redoubled in intensity and accompanied by new and more serious signs. What had begun as a pain in the back became "a grief" in the liver; this grief brought on a "madness in the head" with a flushing, due to fever, of the outer and inner extreme parts. All these distresses were accompanied by an excessive sweating, as if the body were trying to throw off the effects of some internal poison. The last stage of the "sweat," as the canon himself knew—this was the fourth wave to sweep over Europe from England since 1506, and the symptoms were common knowledge—was the overpowering urge to sleep, often as not the sleep of death.

Now von Liechtenfels, after his second crisis, decided to offer any doctor except Paracelsus a hundred guilders to rid him of the disease. It was a gesture of desperation; common knowledge too was the fact that the sweat ran its course, burning either itself or the patient out. There was no generally known cure. The few doctors who, for whatever motive, attended the canon, soon abandoned him to the will of God and the deep sleep.

It was at this point, between bouts of fever, that guild officials approached the desperate clergyman with a suggestion: he must call in Paracelsus. Von Liechtenfels' appeal was known throughout the city. The city doctor could hardly refuse to see any citizen and by appearing, Paracelsus would put himself on the spot. For if the illness continued or, as was probable, concluded tragically, his reputation would be dramatically deflated. And if by some fluke the canon were cured, he would simply withhold the one hundred guilders.

Being a stickler on his honor, Paracelsus would either take the case to court, where guild leaders would serve as jury; or he would fly off the handle and, speaking the truth, would "act in a manner unbecoming to a city official." In his hour of agony, the plot appealed to the good canon; he was looking for some singular act of piety to atone for his sins, and ridding the city of the impossible Paracelsus, a black magician if he had ever seen one, was a godsend. He agreed outright. And so the trap was set.

But Cornelius von Liechtenfels was not to spring the

trap; Johann Froben was. In three days after Paracelsus took his case, the canon had recovered completely. On the fourth day, he sent the magician six guilders, with a note that six guilders was more than enough for the brief time Paracelsus was on the case. Within a week, both were in court. And with the eyes of the city on the court proceedings came the news from Zurich which sprung the trap. Johann Froben had decided to make his grand farewell to the good life by attending the Zurich Fair. And he did just that. At the height of the festivities there, he fell dead. The news relieved the jury of any need to preserve appearances. Paracelsus could not really cure; and when the canon testified that he had never been ill in the first place, that the whole affair had been a hoax to expose the impostor, the jury ruled in favor of von Liechtenfels, the Church, and the glory of God.

When Paracelsus recovered his wits, he cooled the ears of the dignified city fathers and the medicine men with the most savage abuse they were ever to hear; and for good measure, or perhaps to give his boundless contempt enough room, he included past ages in time and all of Europe in space:

You shall follow me! You, Avicenna, Galen, Rhazes! You, gentlemen—of Paris, Montpellier, Germany, Belgium, Vienna. You who inhabit the islands of the sea, Dalmatians and Athenians, Arab and Jew and Greek. No patient shall stay in a corner—all shall follow me. The monarchy of medicine shall be mine! So how do you like "Cacophrastus?" Dirt will be your fare! All the universities and all the old writers put together are less talented than my donkey!

When the police came to his house that night they found him gone. He had not even bothered to pack. His specially forged instruments and a few precious chemicals, Oporinus would bring to him to Colmar in Alsace. All the rest, including his laboratory and house and all the glass-ware, was sold to a gold maker named Thurneyser.

Although Paracelsus would try once more to lead a settled existence, with this fiasco in Basel, Switzerland, the pattern of his life was set.

11

IN COLMAR, Paracelsus waited impatiently for Oporinus to bring the few but precious items which he had specifically singled out in the laboratory. He had been interrupted at the climactic stage of a crucial experiment. Three days after his arrival came news not of Oporinus but from Sebastian Amerbach, who had steadfastly remained his friend: his students and patients were already hard at work smoothing things over, making possible his return to Basel. But to Paracelsus, Basel was past history. He knew better than his enemies how deep was the rift between them. Besides, if the results of his recent experiments proved his theory true, he would be welcomed anywhere in the known world. But where was Oporinus?

It was ten days later that two mules, loaded down from mane to rump with alchemical trappings, clattered down the cobblestones of Colmar, a weary but exultant Oporinus at their head.

Paracelsus looked at the loads with disbelieving eyes.

"What is all this?" he said, pointing. The lead mule was laden with an iron cauldron and several crucibles, with a giant bellows, lead sledges and hammers, with ladles and spatulas and tongs—every conceivable instrument for "cooking" metals.

"Those thieves," said Oporinus, assured of his master's approval. "I couldn't leave this to them."

"The thief is *time*," said Paracelsus with some heat. "You've saved a pile of junk and wasted two weeks! And this poor beast," he said, patting the flank of the second mule, "he's frothing at the mouth. He's on his last legs sure!" Oddly, the exhausted animal seemed to be carrying much less weight—only four large crocks, two on a side.

Paracelsus, whose eyes were scanning the loads for something, lifted the lids of the crocks, but he obviously did not find what he was looking for.

"Quicksilver, master," said Oporinus, with a sly grin.

"This you bring over the mountains? All we need is here."

"But this is from the basement of your house. This batch, it must be almost 'ripe,'" said Oporinus, with an air of injured innocence.

Paracelsus shook his head testily. Oporinus was still waiting for metals to ripen into gold. He had given up trying to straighten him out.

"But where—where are the plants?" said Paracelsus.

"How could we make the pass?" Oporinus shrugged. "I saw a million of them growing in the mountains. I dumped the plants."

"Ach!" Paracelsus threw up his hands in despair. It was harder to translate Paracelsus into Oporinus than German into Greek. Long months he had been experimenting with plants, trying to find one with a mercurial "signature," one which would introduce mercury, in an effective form, into the body. One plant particularly had responded well, and should it prove as effective as he hoped, he would have a clue to eliminating, or at least removing, the symptoms of the dreadful "new disease" which for a generation had been the scourge of Europe.

In the beginning, the "new disease" went by several names. A Dr. Roderigo Diaz of Barcelona, Spain, had in 1521 written a book on the "reptilian disease," so named partly because of the male part which it first affected and partly because of the "bubas" or eruptions it produced. These withered and discolored the skin so that it seemed snakelike. Dr. Diaz, who had extensive first-hand experience with such cases, claimed that this "reptilian disease" was one of the first imports from the New World. Sailors aboard the *Santa Maria,* including Christopher Columbus himself, had contracted the scourge from the witch women of the New World.

From Spain, it spread like wildfire. The basic cause was human nature; but politics also increased its incidence. At precisely this time, Charles VIII of France had decided to invade Italy and had decided, moreover, to use Spanish mercenaries in a lightning campaign. But the campaign was not successful; cities were taken and retaken, and the Italian ladies of Florence and Naples and Rome, who contracted the disease from the Spaniards, infected, in turn, French, German, Swiss, and Slavic soldiers, as well as their own Italian men.

Because the infected Spaniards were fighting under a French banner, they spared their homeland a dishonor and began to call the new disease the *mal Français.* This name, the "French disease," greatly pleased the Germans who lost no time in adopting the name. The French, a logical race, reasoned that since the French soldiers had contracted it in Italy, it should be called the "Italian disease." As for the Italians, they for some reason—perhaps flailing away at the lusty and irreligious Henry VIII— decided to call it the "English disease."

So from the first known incidence of the disease in 1494 until two years after Paracelsus wrote his book on the subject in 1530, the "new disease" served as a grisly propaganda weapon. In 1530, Dr. Girolamo Fracastoro of Verona published a poem, in Latin, about a diseased shepherd called "Syphilis," and the name caught on.

Whatever the grim wit in the names, the disease itself was no laughing matter. A few weeks after contact, scabs or ulcers began to form; and soon there was no part of the body or mind which was immune to infection. In fact, in these first-generation cases the disease had not been "domesticated" and in the bodies of Europeans it took from the very beginning an especially virulent form. The first ulcers often deepened into abscesses, spreading across the surface of the body. And as the disease spread outwardly, it struck with terrifying and unpredictable finality inward, affecting blood and organs and brain. In due course, the flesh literally decayed on the bones, and as pus formed over the graying mass, the smell of rot, pungent and sweet, radiated from the sores.

Because of the incubation period of the disease, its cause was not apparent. Before Paracelsus' book and for a century afterward, it was not known. The disease was simply another scourge from God, one which was to be avoided at all costs. Where did the contagion come from? Did it invade the body through the nostrils? People on the streets trampled each other to avoid the odor. Was it an invisible dark rain through the air? Whispering at close quarters became inexcusably bad manners. Indeed, because of the hideous appearance of the skin, the disease was lumped with other horrific deformations, including elephantiasis, and called "leprosy"; and those victims without money or status were pulled off the streets and confined forthwith to a leprosarium. At first the victims were isolated for a certain number of days, in the manner of the forty-day period, or quarantine, which had worked so well against the plague at Ragusa; but when the disease persisted, the possessions of the stricken were burned, and they were locked up in guarded barracks outside the cities, there to wait for death.

Yet at the same time the powerful not only remained free but a few flaunted their illness. Infected kings who, ironically, were thought to have a healing touch held court with their heavily perfumed ladies in hot and unventilated rooms. The most celebrated victim of syphilis was the German satirist and patriot Ulrich von Hutten who took a curious pleasure both in advertising himself as a martyr to the scourge and in recommending a worthless powdered wood called *guaiacum* as a cure. Ulrich roamed up and down the continent reading his acidic verses and making a gruesome spectacle of himself.

By 1528 Paracelsus had already had first-hand experience with hundreds of syphilitics. He had discovered, and was the first to publish, the source of the disease: physical contact, probably sexual, with an infected person. As to the origin, he rejected the New World import theory and in a burst of nationalism blamed the disease on the French. Meantime, he rejected all external remedies in favor of an organic one which would not only remove the symptoms and eliminate the disease, but reconstitute the man.

The virtues of the metallic salts interested him particularly. He had already contented himself that "poverty of the blood" called for iron, with the understanding that mere iron filings, for instance, were less than useless. "We should," he wrote, "choose a plant which contains iron in etherealized condition."

And for the new disease he worked in a parallel direction. Although a mercury fad had come and apparently gone with nothing but destructive results, his own chemical triad of sulphur-mercury-salt pointed to mercury. Syphilis called for some salt of mercury "etherealized" in herbs or the juices of herbs. And so, for months before publishing a tract in 1528 (the first of an eight-book work) Paracelsus experimented with specially grown herbs, cooking and evaporating, calcining the powder and testing for mercury.

Oporinus, watching all this painstaking work, began to have real doubts. Could it be that the crotchety magician really preferred brewing medicines to cooking gold? Impossible; yet how could he believe otherwise? And suddenly, as an assistant, Oporinus became bumbling and absent-minded. His mood alternated between a kind of arrogant self-defense, when he felt that he had somehow been duped, and an utter boredom.

Once Paracelsus was trying to combine the juice of an herb with the mercury freshly roasted from cinnabar, the sulphurous fumes rolling up inside the alembic. Oporinus moved in so close that Paracelsus could not move freely.

"Is it the recipe for the stone?" said Oporinus, his nose a few inches from the glass.

Paracelsus was fed up. "Yes, Oporinus," he said. "The secret of the ages is before your eyes." Paracelsus stepped in and removed the lid of the alembic, but Oporinus,

greedy for a clue, elbowed him aside. And suddenly
Oporinus found his arm locked behind his back and his
nose pushed through the opening itself. The sulphur fumes
belched upward and for a moment Oporinus' head was
lost in the cloud. Years later, in a deprecatory memoir of
his master, he would write:

His kitchen blazed with constant fire; his *alcali, oleum sublimati,
rex praecipiti,* arsenic oil . . . or God knows what concoction. Once
he nearly killed me. He told me to look at the spirit in his alembic
and pushed my nose close to it so that the smoke came into my mouth
and nose. I fainted from the virulent vapor. . . . Only when he
sprinkled water on me did I come to.

As Oporinus stumbled about gasping and sputtering and
cursing, Paracelsus said, "About the 'stone' you have the
final word."

Oporinus disappeared for a week. His doubts as to
Paracelsus' magic were grave. One possibility remained:
his master did not need to experiment for the stone because he had already found it—found it and kept it hidden
in the hollow pommel of the sword. Why else would he be
so meticulous about keeping it forever at his side? So he
returned, more sullen and absent-minded than ever.

Meantime Paracelsus, experimenting with his etherealized mercury, was noting remarkable effects on the victims
of syphilis. He never wanted for cases. Miserable wretches
in advanced stages of pain and of bodily dissolution came
to him begging for treatment. Paracelsus looked coldly at
each case. If in his judgment the "archaeus," or life-force,
had left the limb or organ or individual, he gently turned
him away; but if he saw "virtue" in the victim, and a
willingness to believe in himself as physician, he attended
him as if he were a king. At length, after dozens of

positive indications, the patient was ready to return to society.

Paracelsus knew better, by now, than to expect anything like a welcome from a medical guild or a school or a town council. So in choosing a town, he looked only for an ideal place to prove his new arcana. He chose Nuremberg: it had a leprosarium with fifteen lepers, few enough to attend with individual care.

As usual now, his reputation preceded him. A chronicler recorded the entrance of Dr. Theophrastus ab Hohenheim, "a peculiar and wondrous man":

He laughs at the doctors and scribes of the medical faculty. They say he burned Avicenna at the University of Basel, and he stands alone against nearly the whole medical guild. He uses his own judicial physics and has contrarieties with many; his practice is against all, and he is another Lucian, so to speak.

Immediately upon his arrival, the doctors of Nuremberg proposed a debate with a challenger. Paracelsus counter-proposed a trial by cures: give him a patient, preferably a syphilitic, whom they had abandoned as hopeless. Had they not abandoned the fifteen patients in the leprosarium? The decision of the guild was immediate and unanimous: he could have the leprosarium in his charge, and welcome.

It was the same story. Paracelsus set to work first to predispose the mind to health. Moving freely among the lepers himself, he began to give their lives order and usefulness. He molded them into a community, stressing cleanliness and exercise, beauty and work. And with new order came new hope. One by one they responded, until all fifteen were asking for chores. The new medicine he administered personally with meals, giving each a dosage suited to himself alone. "And if this doesn't work," he said, patting the pommel of his sword, "this will!" Day by

day the leprosarium became less forbidding, more beautiful; the inmates stronger and more cheerful, until the
citizens of Nuremberg came by to see the flowers or to
hear the lepers serenading each other with the lute.

It was at the leprosarium that Oporinus lost his last
illusion. One of the younger patients, daring to hope for
the first time in a year, had worked beyond his strength.
He was carrying a wooden bucket of water to the com-
munal bath when he keeled over. Immediately, Paracelsus
was at his side.

"No use, Master Paracelsus," gasped the fallen man. "It's
no use."

"Nonsense, Franz," said Paracelsus, cradling his head in
his arm. But he was secretly alarmed. The eyes, dilated,
were dangerously vague. Paracelsus called to Oporinus to
shake "the least grain" from the pommel into a glass of
water and bring it posthaste.

Oporinus brought both the glass of water and the
pommel; the latter he held upside down and shook, trying
without alarming the patient to tell Paracelsus that all
the "most powerful medicine in the world" was used up,
gone.

"Enough, enough, one grain is quite enough," said
Paracelsus, ignoring him. He shook the glass in a circular
motion and applied it to the lips of the leper. In a minute
he was on his feet again, insisting on finishing his chore.

Oporinus worked his mouth without saying anything,
but at last the words came: "That pommel was empty.
The pommel has always been empty!"

"He doesn't believe so," said a grinning Paracelsus,
nodding toward his patient. Then, growing serious, he
said, "If you can understand this secret, Oporinus, you
will know something better than the stone."

The vacant look in Oporinus' eyes took on a shade of contempt. He understood only too well. Paracelsus' enemies were right: he was, in part at least, an impostor.

What Oporinus and the medical guild of Nuremberg could not understand was how Paracelsus, using a mercury salt, etherealized, and an imaginary remedy in a hollow pommel, could have cured nine of the fifteen "lepers." So once again, Paracelsus had dumbfounded and outraged the medical guild through sheer competence; and once again the guild, aided this time by the most powerful commercial trust in Europe, set him scurrying out into the open road.

For with his eyes wide open, Paracelsus had walked into a "war of cures" which had been raging a dozen years. On the one side were the orthodox doctors, or Galenists, who swore by a medication called "guaiacum," the wood of a bush found only in the West Indies. The logic behind these doctors' reasoning was, since the disease originated in the New World, so should its cure. The wood was stripped, pulverized, boiled; it was applied internally in broths and externally in the ever-present poultice.

But the most popular form was a combination smoke-and-steam bath, taken for prescribed lengths of time in an air-tight room. Coals were brought to a white-hot glow beneath a broad, shallow pan of water; and when the air stung with the steam, bundles of guaiac wood were thrown onto the coals. The object was to lie motionless in this mixture of billowing smoke and steam as long as necessary to effect a cure. The beauty of this use of guaiacum was that it acted both externally, acting directly upon the ulcers of the skin, and internally, if the patient were obedient enough to breathe long and deep and thus to heal the vital organs and the blood through the lungs.

Unfortunately though, the smoke smelled putrid; besides causing copious tears and gagging, it induced nausea. Even so, the imported wood was all the rage. The wealthiest trading house in Europe—none other than the Fuggers of Augsburg who owned the lead mines around Villach—had cut in the doctors on the profits and had hired effective advertisers, such as Ulrich von Hutten, to sing its praises. Guaiac wood was, unmistakably, big business.

Opposing the orthodox Galenists were the "metalist" empirics. These doctors, who were at least one rung below the Galenists on the social scale, prescribed mercury. It too was given externally and internally, often with results even more gruesome than the guaiac treatment. In his major book on syphilis, Paracelsus, who gave the most complete description of the symptoms to exist for another two hundred years, brought home the horror and the futility of both methods:

You say even Theophrastus can't help this patient. That the lead club fell down on you. Who could put such murder straight again? This patient you have smoked fifteen times. That one you have balmed fifteen times. Another you have washed fifteen times. And the fourth you led around in the (guaiac) wood. This one you made swallow a quarter pound of mercury, another half a pound or a pound or even a pound and a half. This one has it in his marrow, another in his veins. There it is in a corpse; there a living man goes around with it. There it is in powdered form; there it is sublimated, calcinated, resolved, precipitated, and so on. Who could cover up such a felony?

The work berated both sides mercilessly, calling them fools, thieves and murderers.

On completion of the first chapter, publication was stopped. Paracelsus was informed by Nuremberg aldermen that he must submit all works to be printed to one Dr. Heinrich Stromer, dean of the medical school at the University of Leipzig. Now, it was bad enough for one of Paracelsus' spirit that his freedom to print was suppressed; but when he discovered that the good dean was a business partner with the Fuggers in guaiac trade, he felt the old rage return. But he was wiser now. He did not send off the scathing letter which he had written; instead, he located an underground press and started the publication all over again.

It was about this time that he saw another version of the "bearded spy" of Basel. It was a different man, but with the same look about him, one who was liable to appear at every turn, never outwardly menacing, never melodramatic, yet always, with studied casualness, watching and waiting, like a motionless crow hunched into its feathers, squatting on a dead tree.

Despite Paracelsus' persistence, this major work, *Eight Books on the Origin and Causes of the French Disease,* was not to see the light of day in his lifetime. The press was discovered; the printed chapters and the type which had been set destroyed. And when the Nuremberg magistrates noted the audacious humor on the title page—for Paracelsus had dedicated the illegal publication to one Lazarus Spengler, the secretary of the aldermen—he remembered the "crow" and found himself once again galloping south into the hills. And galloping alone. Oporinus, disillusioned, bitter and secretly shamed that so clever a man as himself had been taken in so long by an impostor, faced a choice. Something deep in himself suggested that Paracelsus was the only sane man in a mad world, whereas every important professional had insisted that Paracelsus was a devil disturbing a divinely ordered status quo. Was it a mad master or a mad world? Oporinus made his choice—he ran away.

Ironically for Paracelsus, had he tried to publish his work two years later, the Fuggers would have paid the printing costs and even, perhaps, promoted its sale. By then they also owned the mercury monopoly. But two years to Paracelsus was an age; in two years he had found himself: he was healing the mind.

IV

AUREOLUS,
THE SAGE

Alterius non sit qui suus
esse potest.

Let no man be another's who
can be his own.

PARACELSUS

12

PARACELSUS! Paracelsus! Paracelsus!"

It was as if now the whole of Europe were one vast canyon into which a commanding voice had broadcast the name, a name which echoed and re-echoed, rising and falling, wherever rumor or fact announced that the gypsy doctor was seen or was coming—a name which was repeated in every register of human opinion or human passion. To different people, Paracelsus meant different things. He was a healer and a scourge; he was a savior and a devil, a criminal and a friend. But to every man, woman and child he was something.

For he was now an Idea. He was the evil Dr. Faust who had sold his soul to the devil; he was the champion of the poor who again and again had flouted authority and lived to tell about it; he was the irascible, the serene, the merry saint who abandoned position, wealth and comfort to live his own truth. He was too big, too real to be true— until he arrived, usually unexpectedly. Perhaps he appeared on a distant hill in the hush of an afternoon; or at a tavern an hour before dawn; or riding his earth-brown mare on a side street on a Sabbath. He appeared, the bald head glistening in the sun rapt inwardly in its own thoughts, the body wearing still the alchemist's jacket, the satchel full of secret medicines, the scrolls of astrological charts and unfinished manuscripts bulging—and always, the huge hangman's sword flopping alongside on the working flanks of the mare.

The children were the first to know of his arrival. Once they lost their terror or their awe, they flocked to his side. He would, as Leeks had done years back, hand them mint or dill and then give the reins of the mare into the hands of the smallest one, asking to be led into town; the others, running and shouting, would return to spread the news: "Papa, it's him, it's Paracelsus! Mama, the gypsy doctor's here!" When the children knew, the whole town knew.

Even in places where he had never been before, the poor folk knew his routine: he headed for the nearest tavern or inn, and there, after guaranteeing the innkeeper half of whatever the proceeds—for each paid something, if only an onion or a wildflower—he rolled out his sheepskin shingle and set up shop. And in a matter of minutes the patients came.

One by one and then in clusters they came, until a long line formed, often extending into the street. Paracelsus from time to time rearranged the line, advancing to the fore emergency cases, children, mothers big with child. The occasional nobleman who appeared, carried by his serfs upon an ornate litter, was usually obliged to wait in line, although if the illness warranted, he advanced. Paracelsus' sense of fairness was absolute. And very soon, as if by magic, the atmosphere of the inn, so rowdy an hour before, took on something of the hush of a chapel. Despite the pain within each, the people were patient and even cheerful, as if the healing had already begun.

After Nuremberg, Paracelsus made no further effort toward respectability. He accepted whatever came along. For months, perhaps to acquaint himself firsthand with the real meaning of poverty—for he could always, now, make a living by practicing medicine—he begged with a wooden bowl, joining the bands of refugees displaced by the continual wars. He learned too well the stinginess of the burgers "who," he said, "begrudge the poor the dish of soup they give and think day and night how they can avoid giving it." Of the homeless poor he said, "They are driven from land to land, and the door is slammed at their approach. More than blessed is he who loves the poor."

At the same time, he did not make a fetish of poverty. He did not use it, like many of the self-styled "saints" of his day as a stance from which to spew a bitterness, a deeper poverty of the soul upon the world. To him, rich people were also people. His fortune suddenly reversed, or his self-imposed discipline over, he accepted at face value the largesse of King Ferdinand of Bohemia who offered to pay the printing costs of his new book. And when the royal treasurer, after the book was printed, refused to deliver the one hundred florins owed the printer, Paracelsus was not even surprised. He presented himself to His Majesty, heard himself called an "impudent swindler," and again moved on. Anger had left him; he seemed to move in and to convey a kind of powerful mildness.

Books now, as a matter of fact, grew out of him. He was like a tree whose harvest had come. What he did not himself write, he dictated to a hired secretary; and the

words came with such speed that, as was written at the
time, "You'd think it was the devil speaking in him." He
was impelled to write. For it was clear to him that his
means for establishing a new medicine, one based upon
"experimenting and reasoning thereon," was not to be a
young generation of doctors trained by himself. The
means, except for a few select men whom he had convinced, were books.

Merciless with himself, he also showed no mercy to his
secretaries. He dictated, often at top speed, for twenty-four
hours at a time without pausing to eat, and when the
secretaries missed passages or misunderstood others, he
scalded their ears. Afterward, as though released of a
burden, he became wonderfully happy. But his books now,
after Nuremberg, no longer stressed medicine as such.
They were concerned with the inner life of man.

The *Greater Surgery Book* which King Ferdinand so
roundly insulted turned out to be the best seller of its day.
It immediately went into a second printing; and within a
half-dozen years, when Paracelsus no longer needed their
support or even cared for success, the orthodox doctors
themselves acclaimed it. Together with such books as
Andreas Vesalius' *De Fabrica Humani Corporis,* it revolu-
tionized surgical practice.

His concern was fully as much ethical as it was techni-
cal; his ideal of a surgeon was not merely one who knew
the joints and handled a keen edge, but one who was an
exceptional man. His first qualifications included "A clear
conscience; A desire to learn and to gather experience; and
A greater regard for his honor than for money." What
personal experience moved him to state that surgeons must
not be "runaway monks" or "men with red beards," we
will unfortunately never know. But that Paracelsus was a

scientist in the highest sense of the word is indicated clearly in one of the qualifications of a good surgeon: "He must not scorn the workings of chance." Paracelsus stood ever ready to reconceive or to drop any theory which did not jibe with the facts of experience.

Trenchant and wise as the qualifications for surgeons were, it was the supplement to the Hippocratic oath which he wrote as a reminder to himself that speaks most eloquently, not only of the medicine of the day but of Paracelsus himself. It furnishes an unexpected look at a beleaguered genius moving in a stultified world:

This, [wrote Paracelsus,] I swear:

to accomplish my system of medicine;

not to waver in its defense as long as God grants me the office;

to oppose all erroneous medicines and doctrines;

to love the sick like my own body;

not to trust my eyes;

not to prescribe medicine without understanding;

not to accept a fee unless it has been earned;

not to trust a pharmacist;

not to guess but to know;

not to treat any prince or gentleman, except I have my fee in my purse;

nor any monk or nun, in particular not in Franconia and Bohemia;

nor any doctor;

nor a person who is unfaithful to wife or husband;

not to undertake any treatment in cases where Nature fails;

to consider beneath my dignity a person who cheats me out of my fee;

to treat men of all sects, but no renegade;

to help women in childbed myself.

The fusion of unflinching determination and humility behind these lines comes from a life of experience and reveals something of the nature of a man unique even among the extravagant men of the Renaissance.

But his great preoccupation now was the realization of his dream: to heal the mind. The bits and pieces which he had been learning, discovering, absorbing all his life formed a single truth, that patients—often with the aid of medicines and more often in spite of them—healed themselves. And so, the secret medicine in the pommel.

This "most powerful medicine in the world" was not the opiate, laudanum, which he was the first to use, it was not Leeks' bitter dandelion pill which, at least, "did no harm," it was not even a sugar "placebo." It was imaginary, it existed only in the mind of the patient. It was "faith"; but the kind of faith which involves more than a mechanical mouthing of words. Rather it was an autosuggestion which brings to bear the will and the passions and the imagination—the whole of the mental, and when possible, the physical powers of the patient.

"Without faith in our ability to walk," he wrote, "we could not walk." Less and less now did he dole out medicines, even of his etherealized metallic salts; more and more he sought tricks, techniques, procedures of bringing the patient to a state of mind in which, consciously in the few and unconsciously in the many, he tapped his own inner powers. One of his key secrets, in his own words, was: "If a person believes in what I say, he will be sure that it will come true, and see it before his imagination. If he goes to bed with this idea strongly entrenched in his mind, he will experience exactly what I told him."

An early experience in self-healing came to him on the banks of the Danube, in Ingolstadt. He was passing through the town when an alderman approached him asking for help. His young daughter had been paralyzed since birth, and all the doctors, herbalist and metalist, those acclaimed as masters throughout the countryside and those denounced as quacks, had tried to cure her and failed. No medicine helped. "In fact," said the alderman, "I can't pay them to come any more." Paracelsus looked at the man. He had had a great success with children, and the devotion of the father for his girl appealed to him. He agreed.

Once at the alderman's home, however, he found the mother absolutely rabid in her resistance to him. Looking into her face, he could hear her arguing against having "that devil, Paracelsus" attend her helpless daughter. Weren't things bad enough already?

But the girl of four, propped on the pillows in the bedroom, delighted him. She was holding a toy boat, a chip of wood with an embroidered little sail, up to her mouth and blowing. Her wide brown eyes, like her mother's but without the anger and grief, were open and receptive.

"Hello, Emma," said Paracelsus, standing at the foot of the bed, showing his affection with a big smile.

The girl looked at him sharply, decided that he was all right, and returned the smile. Paracelsus moved to the stool at her side.

"Touch her and I kill you," hissed the mother.

"I will not touch your daughter, Mama," said Paracelsus mildly.

"Nor feed her pills blessed by the devil himself!"

The mother was disturbing the girl. Paracelsus handed her the satchel; she could keep all his medicines herself, he said, but she must wait outside. After some gentle urging by the father, the mother relented, but she took with her, very cautiously, the black magic which she knew to be in the pommel of the sword. So Paracelsus was left with nothing.

Gently, he pulled back the covers of the bed and examined the legs. The muscles lacked tone, they were a bit flabby from disuse; but they were beautifully formed.

"These legs are perfect, perfect," he said, smiling happily at the girl.

She smiled back. "But they don't go," she said.

"Who says they don't?" he said in a powerful, glad voice which filled the room. He pulled up the covers, rose, and went over to the window. The morning sun cast a molten glow across the river.

"What a day to sail boats in the river, eh Emma?" he said.

"It would be fun . . . ?"

"Theo. My name is Theo."

". . . Theo," the girl concluded. "This is a Spanish galleon."

Paracelsus described the joys of walking, of climbing, of dancing, he described for her how the spirit within her was waiting for her to really give her legs a try. What's more, he said, he had seen hundreds of thousands of legs both good and bad and he had never seen more perfect legs than hers. When the girl was livid with excitement and eager to try, he said:

"Not yet, Emma. Now you must rest. But when you wake, you will come join us in the kitchen." Soothingly now, he had her repeat, over and over as a simple fact, "The legs are perfect, perfect." A few minutes afterward, the girl was in a profound sleep.

Two hours had gone by. Paracelsus, with Emma's father, sat in the kitchen watching the mother setting out soup for lunch, thumping bowl and spoon and pot with a mounting fury. The alderman went over to his wife hoping to calm her, but after a few minutes it was obvious to Paracelsus that he had lost. He came over and stood timidly, holding out three gold coins.

"Thank you for coming."

"No, no," said Paracelsus, rejecting the coins. "I haven't earned them, have I?"

And now, the mother was suddenly kind. Few men rejected gold; and the devil's disciple, who had done little harm so far, was about to go.

"You could at least take a bowl of soup," she said gruffly, as she fetched another bowl.

The three had scarcely pulled their chairs to the table when the curtain in the doorway moved. And there, one hand on the frame and the other carefully carrying the "galleon," was Emma, smiling through a very real physical effort and a very deep excitement. The mother gave a shriek of disbelief and joy which seemed to freeze in her throat, as, one tentative step after another, Emma moved shakily toward Paracelsus, who himself was half-risen from his chair.

"Oh, Theo," she said happily, "could we sail one together?"

And then they were all outside, the magician and the girl on their hands and knees, the parents standing behind them, watching the wind nudge the embroidered sail into the stream as, inside, the soup cooled in the three bowls.

And so it was. From that incident, in 1526, on, Paracelsus concentrated upon disorders of the mind, and more than once did the image of his mother, Elsa, well up before his eyes. There was the young mother who, abandoning her children, spent her days running up and down the street in a fit of excitement, blurting forth words about rags and dishes and hair as if they were inspired "from beyond." With exceeding gentleness Paracelsus approached her and, talking through her words, he entered her speech, her thought, her world, until by voice and gesture and idea he had calmed her mind. Speechless at last, blinking, breathless, she stood before him as though she had after years of trying stepped down off a treadmill.

There was the matron with her wide eyes weeping "at the world." Her own children had grown and gone, and she sat on the curb watching the endless stream of destitute strangers, muttering about their grief. Paracelsus taught her a spiritual song with a cheerful lilt, and set her to the task of churning the milk of her lone cow into butter for the refugees.

There was the spinster, a "harmless witch" with the laughing sickness, whom he cured by commanding her to fix her mind intently upon the point of light in a magic yellow stone.

There was the entire convent stricken by St. Vitus's dance, a dozen girls compulsively dancing, but abruptly and mechanically like marionettes, their arms and legs, their heads and their hips jerked sharply as if by some demonic puppeteer. For these, he found musicians and ordered them to strike up a melody with a strong beat. Soon, the music had "captured" the spasmic movements of the dance, had gradually made them voluntary, so that they followed the rhythm of the tune. Then, altering the meter, gradually slowing it down until the spasms stopped altogether, he brought the exhausted girls to rest.

At length he seemed to see in the face of all women not so much Elsa's face but the face of the Great Mother of all forms, each individual a divine, a unique variation of the one. By 1540, he had attended so many of the "bewitched" and the "possessed," with such striking success, that there was scarcely a person who doubted that, black magic or white magic, Theophrastus Paracelsus was a master magician.

Paracelsus did not discourage these beliefs. According to his philosophy, one which he had *lived,* Nature herself was magic. He had unveiled many of her secrets, discovered many of her laws, through the new chemistry, but he had *explained* nothing. Man, he wrote, cannot explain the alchemy of a mineral finally and utterly; he cannot account for the virtue of an herb or the powers of the mind or the smile of a child. Nature fulfills the reason and goes beyond it; and he, Paracelsus, was a part of Nature. He was a microcosm, a world-in-little fully as miraculous as the macrocosm, the world-in-all, a tiny world which, in quality, contained the greater world and which, through a correct use of free choice and the grace of God, had seen the perfection in both.

And did this vision show himself to be better, superior, different from other men? Not a whit. But he had at last perfected a technique taught him years ago by Trithemius, a way of knowing himself by turning his attention inward, upon his own mind, in the meditative trance. In one of his later books on the mind, *De Imaginibus,* he described the trance as a "passionate, sympathetic contemplation" rather than the dispassionate sorting out of facts of his younger days as a scientist; and then he proceeded to picture the state in detail:

The soul, in an ecstatic state, is self-centered. The person is blind and deaf. His nose does not smell anything, his hands cannot feel anything. Though he can see, he does not know what he sees. He may hear people talk but does not understand the words. He may grasp for something but is unconscious of what he holds in his hands. Such a person seems to be deprived of his senses and the world thinks him an accomplished fool. In reality he is the wisest man before God, who lets him know His secrets better than all the wise men in the world.

And so for Paracelsus, the scientific method of an endless pursuit of facts about externals no longer bore fruit; in order to understand itself, the mind must turn inward.

Once more he returned to Villach—only to find that Wilhelm had died, a beloved and respected citizen, four years before. So be it, he thought; a cycle was complete. Standing over his father's grave, it occurred to him that his own cycle would soon, would prematurely be complete. To some hamlet or city, upon some countryside nearby— nearby, for he had had enough of harangues and hair- breadth escapes—the crows would return early.

Something dreadful was near, something which he must face unflinchingly. Numberless faces ill and well, friendly and spiteful passed before his inner eye and he wrote, "We have warred for a long time. They drove me out of Lithuania and Prussia, and from Poland, and still it was not enough for them. The Dutch did not like me either, nor the schools, neither Jews nor monks. But, thank God, the patients liked me." Anger he had known, blunder he had made, but he had never been covert and petty; his cross, the divine intertwining snakes about the spine of

light, he had always held high. The great dread was upon
him and he wrote a prayer to his God:

So I have traveled throughout the land and was a pilgrim all my
life, alone and a stranger feeling alien. Then Thou has made grow in
me Thine art under the breath of the terrible storm in me.

As for hatred, how could he hate? Had he not seen the
most confirmed, the most rabid of his enemies thaw with
love when he became a patient? Even the steady, un-
hurried wingbeat of the crows was full of the dark beauty
of Law, they were the sacred scavengers who prepared
the earth for the next generation, the next rain of the
tongues of fire of the Holy Spirit.

On the twenty-fourth day of September, 1541, at the
age of forty-eight, Philippus Theophrastus von Hohenheim,
called by the world Paracelsus, was dead.

Seldom in history have the circumstances surrounding
the death of so famous a man been so obscure. The date,
the place and the fact of Paracelsus' death are clear; every
other detail is subject to multiple interpretations.

The official version of his death seems well calculated to
keep in line the wavering faithful of a Church in turmoil.
According to this version, this extraordinary being who all
his life had steadfastly symbolized a creative rebellion
against what he called "stone churches," discovered an
orthodox piety on his deathbed and meekly returned to
the fold.

Proof, it maintained, lay in a will written only three
days before—written not in his own hand, it is true, but
by a petty official, a notary named Kalbsohr. This will
shows him to be a model of religious penitence who doles

out a few guilders to a remote relative and to the poor, and asks that psalms be sung during his funeral.

But discordant notes arise. For, strangely, this man who decried the luxury of doctors, who was notorious for his habit of sleeping in his clothes and giving his once-soiled outfits to the poor, left a rich and gaudy wardrobe; and even more strangely, for all the care he took with his few remaining guilders, he left no literary executor, no provision for the many books scattered throughout Europe, books which he considered his legacy to mankind and his hope for a new medicine.

Moreover, this official version promotes at least two discordant causes of death. Three days before, for the writing of the will, Paracelsus, it maintained, was too weak to write; and yet the immediate cause of his death was an accidental blow on the head during a drunken brawl in a tavern. And for good measure, it loosed a welter of supporting rumors, all designed to discredit the dead man: since early childhood, Paracelsus had suffered bone deformation from a disease which is today called rickets; he was hopelessly addicted to opium, which was the medication he kept in the pommel of his sword; and finally, he had lived the life of a eunuch.

Small wonder that the poor, whom he had championed all his life, quietly but absolutely rejected the official view. Their great friend and teacher had been held under constant surveillance, a virtual prisoner, in Salzburg by the doctors' guild; he had been slowly, methodically poisoned, and when despite the gradual depletion of his health he had hung on, they had hired an assassin to dispatch him.

Immediately upon his death, his name passed into legend. It was not mentioned publicly; for some reason it was bad manners to do so. But underground, the name lived and grew. Everything about him took on a kind of transfiguration. It was not only the sword, but his horse acquired the ability to perform wonders of transportation, crossing unheard of distances always to arrive in the nick of time for another miraculous cure. Patients at widely separated points swore that they had been attended by Paracelsus at the same time.

Paracelsus had written of an experiment which artificially produced life in the form of a "homunculus," and the story was current after his death that he himself had almost risen from the dead. He had ordered his body to be drawn and quartered and buried in a mound of horse manure, which alchemists knew to be a source of tremendous heat, there to remain for forty days. But an overanxious disciple hurried too quickly through the ritual; and when the body was recovered it had in fact grown together again, but the final crucial moment when the spirit reoccupied it had not been permitted to come!

Of the skeleton which all except the most fanatical followers maintained to be that of Theophrastus Paracelsus, one startling fact is irrefutable: when, some fifty years after burial, it was exhumed to be given a resting place more honorable in the eyes of men, the back of the skull showed a deep fracture.

EPILOGUE

Shortly before his death Paracelsus had numbered the doctors whom he had converted to the new "iatrochemistry." They were few. "Of all the doctors I have brought forth," he wrote, "only two remained in Pannonia, three in Poland, three in Saxonia, one in Slavonia, one in Bohemia, one in Holland—but none in Swabia. Yet there are many who have twisted my teachings to suit their own minds." And judging by the reaction in the first twenty years after his death, his failure was complete. His name lived underground, in a legend; publicly it lived not at all. Polite society had rejected him utterly. Even his disciples denied him in public.

But his truth—the science of his work and the art of his life—polite society could not reject. His cures worked, and even when they did not, a great new concept had entered medicine. Until his coming the new "metalist" doctors had waged a losing war with the Galen-inspired "herbalists." Paracelsus came along and showed them how. He showed them that their metals were, as the Galenists insisted, poisons and showed that these poisons, given in correct doses only, could cure.

Moreover, he demonstrated how the metalist medications could be "etherealized"; the iron of a rusty spike might be destructive, the iron in calf's liver supportive of life. Without fanfare, indeed, without dreaming of its tremendous importance to medicine after him, he introduced a

new concept, of "biochemistry," and was the first to practice the science.

Galenism died hard; it had power and tradition on its
side. But by the end of the sixteenth century, some fifty
years after Paracelsus' death, the study of chemistry and
of chemical medicines was fast becoming an obsession.
Books on the subject in unprecedented numbers rolled off
the presses of Europe. Gradually an entire school of doctors, many of whom also "twisted his teachings," adopted
his name and called themselves "Paracelsians." By this
time even the entrenched orthodoxy listed dozens of
"metallist" compounds in their *materia medica*. Among
the accolades which Paracelsus was to win came one from
Robert Boyle, the "father of modern chemistry," a hundred years after his death:

> Chymists have put some men in hope of greater cures than formerly
> could be thought possible. Before men were awakened by the many
> promises and some cures of Arnaldus de Villanova and Paracelsus,
> many physicians used to pronounce a disease incurable. They would
> rather discredit the art and detract nature than confess that the two
> could do what ordinary physick could not.

But true to the law of the magi, that man's great work,
his *magnum opus*, is never something outside himself,
Paracelsus lived so that his life itself was a work of art.
Scattered and fragmentary though the facts are, they continue to astound his biographer, and the power of them
created a new prototype for the arts. In the generation
after his death the story was widespread, particularly
among simple folk, of a brilliant man who, having mastered all knowledge which the schools could offer, longed
for more. He happened upon the means of tapping the
occult powers of his own mind, powers which enabled
him to perform miracles.

Heavenly—or was it demonic?—forces did his bidding. He could transmute lead into gold, he could produce fruits out of season, he could for a time command the souls of other worlds to revisit his own. But for these powers he paid a price: he had sold his own soul to the devil, and at the foredoomed hour the devil would have his due. And the hour, inevitably, terribly, came. But was it the hour of damnation or of salvation? Did the devil claim him as his own, or did God, pleased that one mortal at least had not been content with the dull, the routine, the mundane, interpose at the last minute and reclaim the prodigal son?

Puppeteers across Europe took up the legend, played the story in the market place. In 1587, a *Book of Dr. Faustus* appeared. And soon thereafter, in the kindred spirit of Christopher Marlowe, Paracelsus—disguised and debased—was stalking and stomping across the revitalized Elizabethan stage. The Marlowe play, *The Tragical History of Dr. Faustus,* continued to be successful for some twenty-five years and even today commands great talents and big houses. And ever since Marlowe, in drama, in poetry, in music, as himself or disguised as Faustus, Paracelsus lives on.

If biochemistry continues to redefine his concepts, if it has far outstripped his applications, it has yet to heed adequately his injunction to treat the whole man rather than the symptom. And as for the mastery of the mind— despite the advent of psychology and psychiatry and psychoanalysis, with their grudging acknowledgment of extrasensory perception and the praise of such of their pioneers as Carl G. Jung—we have as yet no viable rule to fathom this man's depth and his reach.

INDEX